Then began Lt. Obenauf's heroic adventure. For what he did that April night he was awarded the Air Force's highest peacetime decoration, the Distinguished Flying Cross, and made an aircraft commander — at 23, one of the youngest to hold such a position in SAC.

Here is an incomparable true adventure story, full of excitement and suspense. It is also a moving testament to the seemingly limitless resources of the human spirit.

# TWENTY SECONDS TO LIVE

# Twenty Seconds to Live

By

*ELIZABETH LAND*

E. P. DUTTON & CO., INC.

NEW YORK          1959

LIBRARY OF CONGRESS CATALOG CARD NUMBER: 59–12566

*To the 341st Bomb Wing,
the 10th Bomb Squadron in particular*

# ILLUSTRATIONS

*(Between pages 16 and 17)*

# TWENTY SECONDS TO LIVE

# CHAPTER I

When Binbrook one-six took off that evening, there was no sense of impending disaster. Except for a few minutes delay in the take-off, everything was routine. The plane taxied down the taxistrip and pulled out onto the runway. The pilot put in his call to the tower.

"Dyess tower, Binbrook one-six. We're ready to roll."

"Roger, Binbrook one-six. You're cleared to take off."

The pilot reached out and pushed six blue-handled throttles up to 100 per cent power, flicked a switch on his instrument panel, and, in an instantaneous and controlled process, water began mixing with fuel.

As all six engines reached a whining peak, the giant wings quivered with vibration, and six black columns of smoke shot from the tail pipes of each engine. The pilot put more pressure on the foot brakes to hold the big jet back and watched as the needles on the engine instruments settled at the proper indications. When they hung steady, he released the brakes, and the plane quickly began to gather speed as she rolled down the runway. Faster and faster and faster until she lifted herself.

The six streams of black smoke streaked backward as she began to climb. A thousand feet. Two thousand. She cut the sky clean. Three thousand. Four thousand. The whine had almost died. Five thousand. Six thousand. She disappeared from sight.

# CHAPTER II

As Lieutenant James Obenauf, co-pilot of the B-47, sat in his seat that night, he prepared for a routine mission. They were going to Denver and "bomb" Dalhart, near Amarillo, Texas on the way. Lieutenant John Cobb, the navigator-bombardier (or observer, as his position was sometimes referred to) was getting an evaluation check ride. Every so often each man, regardless of how long he'd been flying, had a flight proficiency check, and tonight they had a Standardization Board evaluator with them, Major Joe Maxwell, to do the checking on Cobb. By leaning out of his seat to his left and looking down the crawlway, Obie could see Joe Maxwell's back.

Joe was sitting on a metal folding chair, and he didn't look very comfortable. As fourth man in the plane, he was an extra, and, since there is no seat built into the body of the ship for anyone riding in the fourth man position, he had brought his own chair along and set it up behind Cobb. That way he could look over Cobb's shoulder from his place in the crawlway and check on what Cobb was doing.

Obie couldn't see Cobb. The observer's position is in the nose of the ship; the pilot's and co-pilot's positions are up under the canopy, like a tandem bicycle with the pilot in front of the co-pilot. From the platform on which their seats are mounted to the floor of the crawlway is a good two to three feet so that the observer cannot be seen unless the pilot or co-pilot steps down from his seat into the crawlway itself.

The co-pilot is also separated from the pilot, who sits directly in front of him, by an instrument panel set with dozens of dials and gauges arching from left to right. These instruments and a protruding piece of metal about a foot long and four inches wide jutting up from behind the pilot's seat which acts as a headrest, prevents the co-pilot from seeing anything directly in front of him. As a matter of fact, nothing can be seen of the pilot except the back of his head, which is encased at all times in a helmet.

The helmet is important for more reasons than mere protection. It contains the means by which the crew communicates with each other. A microphone is set in the oxygen mask, which buttons across each face, and, by speaking into it, a person's voice is communicated to the others through earphones set in the helmet. When the co-pilot wants to talk to the pilot or the observer, he presses a mike button on the half-wheel which tops the column in front of him and holds the button down. On releasing the button, his voice cuts off, leaving the system open for reply. In similar fashion, the pilot communicates with the co-pilot and observer.

The observer's mike button, on the other hand, is set in the floor of the ship and is operated with one foot. There are several reasons for this; for one, it leaves his hands free to make the constant computations his job requires, and for another, he has no column for the button to be placed on. The column is to the B-47 what the steering wheel is to a car, and by means of pulling it back or pushing it forward, the ship gains or loses altitude. The observer's job is not to steer the ship, except on one occasion: the last few minutes out from target, at which time he guides it by means of a special handgrip (called the dead man's stick) which is set in his work table directly in front of his right hand.

While it is necessary to push the mike button in order to transmit speech, it is not necessary to push anything in order to hear. The system stays open to all ears at all times, so that what one man says to another all three men can hear. This is very important since all three jobs are so closely interwoven that whatever is said is likely to be of interest to them all.

As a further and more far-reaching means of communication, the microphone is used for receiving and relaying messages from one ship to another and from a ship to the ground. Thus it is that each man's earphones are filled with a constant cacaphony of sound; static, garbled words, and voices coming in from other planes or ground stations many miles away. It is possible to cut out these voices and leave the system open only to those in the ship, but the pilot and co-pilot leave theirs open at all times in order to receive any messages from the ground, or distress signals another ship may send. If so many voices are confusing in the beginning, the situation quickly straightens itself out. A man's ear soon learns to know the voices of his own crew and to pick them out of the mess. He is also aided by the fact that the voices of the men within the plane usually come in more clearly.

This instantaneous means of communication is very important in the B-47, since physical movement is limited to just about nil. The days when a man could leave his seat and go tap on another man's shoulder died with the age of the jet. It is now more important that the space formerly given over to moving around be reserved for fuel.

The B-47 is a powerhouse and drinks fuel as if it were lemonade. In the hollows of her belly, enormous compartments hold the fuel. Fuel is also stored in the tip tanks, which are attached like big silver torpedoes beneath each of the wings. The ship is almost like a flying fuel tank, and, whereas in the old days men often had time and enough to bail out of a burning ship, they now may not get out at all. She can blow up on the instant.

With so much fuel aboard, the dangers if an explosion occurs are greatly increased, but by means of such an extensive storage system, the B-47 can remain aloft for a much longer period of time than she could otherwise. She can stay up about eight hours without refueling, and most practice missions are planned for that length of time. Each crew keeps a chart showing fuel consumption right to the minute. This information is so vital that it is necessary to prepare stacks of reports and forms before the men ever leave the ground. Mission planning takes many hours, and the men have a saying: "When the paper weighs as much as the aircraft, it's time to take off."

Ten hours strapped in the seat of a B-47 can seem a very long time. The men sit on top of a survival kit, which is made of metal covered with canvas, and that's what it feels like. There is one of them strapped to each man's rear-end in case he has to bail out. The kit holds everything from wool socks to fishing tackle. The list includes fruitcake. It is a handy little gadget weighing forty-two pounds, and it has saved lives from time to time, but it is the devil to sit on.

Two other parts of their equipment do not make for comfort. They are the parachute, which is strapped to each man's back (all but the man who flies as an extra, like Joe Maxwell, who sometimes carries a chest pack, which he keeps close at hand in order to put on in case of an emergency), and there is the helmet itself. The helmet weighs a dead six pounds. Six pounds doesn't sound like much, but by the time a man's worn one a couple of years, his neck develops special muscles.

The seats in the B-47 look like nothing so much as an electric chair and are about as comfortable. Spare and rigid, they are rigged with explosive charges to catapult a man out of the plane in the event the ship has to be abandoned.

As for the ship's interior, the crawlway *is* a crawlway. It is hard for a man to stand. He doesn't have to get down

Lieutenant James E. Obenauf, co-pilot

Major Joe Maxwell, navigator-observer

Major James Graves, aircraft commander

Lieutenant John Cobb, navigator-bombardier

A B-47 in flight over Abilene, Texas

on his hands and knees, but he does have to stoop. It is a kind of stomach-shaped aisle hollowed out of the left hand side of the ship. It measures two feet wide by four feet high and leads from the pilot's and co-pilot's positions up under the plastic canopy down into the nose, where the observer sits. It would be difficult to walk it even without a 'chute and survival kit on. With them, progress is delayed and blundering.

Uncomfortable and confining as it is, for almost two years it had been Obie's world, and he had long since become accustomed to it and the regimen it required. In the time he had been flying her, he had learned a lot about the B-47; enough to regard her with respect and admiration laced with moments of awe. This respect and admiration was the closest he could come to love. To love a B-47 would have been like loving the wrong end of a Roman candle. He called her "the beast" or "the brute," and he watched her warily. He had learned that you had to fly her or she'd fly you.

All in all, it was a very different world from the one he had known as a boy. The supercharged ways of the Strategic Air Command were keyed to the adrenals, and, until now, he'd never been called on to exercise anything like such constant alertness or immediate action. Life on a farm in Illinois had never demanded more than milking cows, plowing fields, and putting in a crop. Even then his duties were not pressing, since he was the youngest of nine children, and, until he was of high-school age, there were always the older boys to help his father.

The Obenaufs were a German Catholic family and lived in a big farmhouse, which sat on a flat spot near the main road out from the little town of Mundelain, forty miles from Chicago. The house was surrounded by fields of oats, corn, and alfalfa, and big maples shaded it in the summer. From his window, Obie could see the rim of a little lake where he sometimes went swimming or fishing.

Half a mile down the road was the parochial school. By the time he reached school age, there was only himself and Paul and Luella left to make the mile 'round trip. Ralph and Larraine and Bob had left home to get married; Helen went to high school in town, and Dorothy and Gertrude were working.

As the two youngest in the family, he and Paul were pretty close, although with something of the Germanic nature from which he was descended, Obie seldom showed or shared his emotions. This was not to say he had none. It was simply that emotions had a deeply personal quality and were to be dealt with in private. What he felt, what he thought, he kept to himself.

The Obenaufs had a rough time of it during the depres-

sion as a lot of people did, but their German frugality saw
them through, and by the time Obie was born, they were
doing all right. They built a new house and put in elec-
tricity and a basement heating system; his father bought
a couple of tractors, and his mother had all the electrical
conveniences in her kitchen. The Obenaufs always put
their money where it showed, never being ones for frip-
peries, and little by little they established themselves. This
was the time that Obie knew; not the harder one which
had preceded it.

As the youngest of the family, it might have been expected that he would have been subject to special favors,
but it often seemed to him that he had been born for the
specific purpose of catching it coming and going from his
oldest brother on down. His sisters took delight in bossing
him, for which he had little defence. Mostly, he tried to
stay out of their way and keep them out of his. This
worked pretty well. When it was inevitable that their
paths should cross, however, he resorted to mute retalia-
tion in the form of frogs (dead or alive) in their dresser
drawers, and snakes (usually alive) under their pillows.

After school he spent his time playing baseball or building model planes, both of which he loved. He had an assortment of pictures on his wall of all the baseball greats
along with pictures of planes. He split his time between

the sand lot and the hay loft, where he would launch his newly finished model plane. When he had tired of sailing it down, he often put a firecracker in the cockpit, lighted it, and sent the doomed ship on its way. The resultant mid-air explosion made for a spectacular climax.

The years between plane-building and high-school graduation were a series of episodes reflecting the inventiveness of the growing Jim Obenauf. During his first year in school, he and Paul used Hallowe'en as an occasion to spatter a schoolroom with rotten apples, a prank from which he would have emerged unscathed had it not been for his collie dog named Pal, who followed them. She was seen by one of the nuns as he and Paul retreated that night, and the next day he was given the third degree. Pressed to admit his guilt, he confessed and the nun told his parents, but for the first time being the baby paid off. His folks decided Paul should be the one punished, since Jim was too young to know any better.

A similar incident involved a snowball fight on a school bus, during which several windows got knocked out. He would have emerged unscathed from this one too, since he was not indicted by the authorities, but when the other participants were called up to the principal's office, he went too, feeling he ought to admit his part in it. This one they won in the principal's office by sheer weight of numbers, however, since there were too many of them (seventeen) to be punished.

During the whole course of his school career, he gave short shrift to his studies. If he made D's, he was satisfied; C's were for the wise guys. There was a half year of algebra he wished might have been different, since his good friend Mr. Hoadley was teaching it, but algebra held onto her mysteries right up to the last.

As a suitable finale to high school, he took part in the senior play. He'd never been in a play before and had no wish to be, but there he was, playing the part of a dumb, big-shot butcher with mustache and apron. If it hadn't been for the disguise, he would never have seen it through.

Then, with a suddenness he neither liked nor anticipated, he was on that same stage getting his diploma. Where the years had gone he didn't know. He'd never been conscious of time. A kind of lackadaisical nonchalance had pervaded his life, and, with few duties and fewer cares, he had simply grown up. Aware for the first time of the future, he gave it a look. He had no desire to go to college, nor had his folks pressed him about it, although, with all eight of the other children through school, he might have gone had he wished. Since he did not wish, being drafted was a certainty. This was fine with him, since it gave him an excellent excuse for joining the Air Force, which he'd always wanted to do anyway.

He'd already had a taste of flying from lessons he took the year before he graduated, having earned the money for them by helping a neighbor farmer spray his fruit trees. He had cherished a childhood dream of playing pro baseball, but when he got up in the air, he knew flying was for him.

He would not be able to go directly into pilot training, however, since he hadn't had the required two years of college. He would have to go in for two years, get out and go to college, then go back in the Air Force, which was the long way 'round, but it couldn't be helped. He had only been in a short time, however, when the Air Force changed the requirements. He could take pilot training if he passed a qualifying examination, which he did.

He was pretty excited about a chance to fly, but with cadet training, life suddenly hit him in earnest. For the first time, grades really mattered, and he wished that he'd taken greater interest in them. Now he was put into classes with fellows who had had those two years of college, and it was really rough.

The squeeze play lasted through primary and basic and right up to advanced. He was barely hanging on when he got to Williams Air Force Base in Arizona. Then he walked out on the flight line one day and laid eyes on his first jet. It was like seeing a girl for the first time and knowing you wanted to marry her. He had the feeling that he was home.

He used to go out on the flight line even before they let him fly, and stand there and look at them. He thought they were the most beautiful things he'd ever seen, and after he flew one, he knew that he'd been right. He seemed to know instinctively what the airplane could do and was as comfortable in that cockpit as he was in his own bed. His flying grades rose immediately, and soon there was no longer any possibility of his washing out. He got his wings in 1955 and orders to report to Dyess Air Force Base in Abilene, Texas. But before he went to Dyess, there was a matter of some importance to be taken care of. He was going back to Illinois and marry a girl named Pat Conner.

Down on one of the lakes about four miles from his home, Pat spent the summers with her parents in a summer cottage. Obie had known who she was ever since she was big enough to throw rocks at, and that was about as close as they got to each other during their younger years. To him, she was just a girl with a husky voice and freckles, and he couldn't have cared less. At that age, girls fell in the same category with school grades. They were for the birds. In later years he saw her occasionally, sitting in the bleachers when he played baseball or at the drugstore in town, but neither paid the other much attention until, quite by chance, a friend got them a blind date. Obie was fifteen at the time, and Pat a year younger.

After that, there were occasional visits to see her when she moved back into Chicago with her parents for the winter, but it was a fifty-mile round trip to her house, fighting traffic all the way, so what with the traffic and the stiff gasoline bill and the time it took to get there, a considerable dent was put in the romance. There continued, therefore, nothing more involved or complicated than minor summer romance in the succeeding four years, and then one day they were both grown up and in love. He was nineteen and home on leave for the first time, when he asked her to marry him as soon as he got his wings.

When the time came for the wedding, however, he had to report to Dyess before he could get a week-end leave, so he could not be in Chicago for any of the preliminaries. He got there the night before the wedding, but not in time for rehearsal, so that during the ceremony he felt somewhat lost. He finally decided his best bet was simply to follow Pat around and do whatever she did, which worked out pretty well. Except for minor difficulties near the end, when she couldn't get his ring on because she'd bought it a size too small, and once when he stepped on her train, everything went smoothly.

He had to leave the next day in order to be back at Dyess. It was a new base, and there was a lot of work to be done, so he couldn't be spared for long. Pat came a day later, and they had a honeymoon slightly interfered with by the fact that he had to spend more time at the base than he did at home, but this was part of the pattern of SAC they were both beginning to know.

There is nothing else quite like it in any other branch of the service. While all military personnel are theoretically subject to twenty-four-hour duty, they are rarely called upon to perform it, but the very backbone of the Strategic Air Command is based on a constant alert system which subjects each man to many twenty-four hour days of alert duty per month. During this time, a man doesn't even go home. He spends his days and nights with the two other men in his crew in a military wedlock that allows for no separations. If one man wants to go to a show (which a crew is allowed to do so long as they stay on the base), he can go only if the other two men in his crew go with him. If the majority vote is a movie and the other guy has already seen it, that's just too bad. He goes anyway.

During this alert duty they sleep in a special barracks, they dress in flight suits, carry revolvers, and have a special-alert crew car to drive. When the klaxon, the alarm system designating an alert, goes off with its harsh grind, the men hit the crew cars running, and, in something less than fifteen minutes they are ready to take off. A number of planes are always standing in constant readiness to take to the sky on the instant.

Over and over and over the alert is drilled into them, until a man can zipper a flight suit with his eyes shut and be out the front door before he really gets them open. On occasions when an alert is the real thing, instead of practice, not only the alert crews go into action, but everybody on the base.

Periodically, SAC calls practice alerts to test the readiness of its bases. With the simultaneous snarls of alert klaxons throughout the command, bases whip themselves within minutes into fighting shape.

When world affairs reach a crisis stage, SAC can increase its alert posture to prepare for the possibility of war. This is called a world-wide alert, and in SAC, it has a special meaning for base personnel and their families. In the summer of 1958, during the Lebanon crisis, SAC had more aircraft on alert than any time in its history. To get those aircraft ready took a lot of work. It meant almost continuous duty for base personnel from the beginning of the alert until the world situation had relaxed sufficiently to return to normal readiness. SAC's men and their families have learned to live with these occasional world-wide alerts and the resulting extra duty that may keep the men away from home for days.

During the build-up, men swarm all over the ramp, performing whatever function is necessary for getting the planes off. Some strap on the ATO, the auxiliary rocket fuel bottled in gray containers and strapped on the fusilage near the tail. When a plane is carrying a heavy weapon, extra thrust helps get the plane up faster. That's what the ATO is for.

Other men patrol the ramp in fire trucks, their red lights going 'round and 'round and 'round. They are there because of the fire hazard created in handling the highly inflammable fuel. Still others drive especially designed yellow tractors, which carry the bombs. They come through a heavily guarded gate in steady procession, carrying the bombs in enormous box-like coffins, which are appropriately covered in black. Guards ride on the back of escort trucks—one to each caterpiller—and each one holds a gun.

The command post at wing headquarters is now similarly guarded. The minute the alert is sounded, sentries are posted around the building and the walks leading to it. At the front door, a man with a rifle challenges anyone's entrance. Outside headquarters in the half-moon drive-way, a staff car sits, its motor running. If the Colonel has to hit the flight line, nobody will have to stop long enough to even start the engine.

In the message center, coded messages come in, and, so swiftly you can almost feel it, things reach a climax.

For the first time, it occurs to a person watching, what it would mean if the planes do take off. Quite possibly, this pattern is being repeated by the Russians, as well as ourselves, and you have the feeling that the whole world is tightening.

Ready now, the base waits. Hours, days, weeks. When the build-up has been completed, there is nothing else to do. Days and nights are spent in the barracks, and there is coffee through the long hours, along with spates of conversation. As if in a conscious effort to take the edge off, the men talk, sometimes jokingly about the things they know best, about things like home.

"Mice? Man they're everywhere! One fell in the toaster last Sunday and got electrocuted. We haven't had toast in a week."

About kids: "No, she's just big enough to pull herself up in her playpen. Then she stands there and hollers because she can't get back down."

About flying: "And I looked in the scope and said,

'What the hell's *that*?' It was Oakie City and I was supposed to have us over Tulsa!"

About civilians: "The lousey feathermerchants just sit
around on their cans. I asked a man the other day, 'How
many civilians work at this base?' and he said, 'Oh, about
half of 'em.' "

About wings: "Don't forget, buddy, we brought in
that trophy for the 341st in the bombing competition. It's
there. Right there under glass."

And about losses: "And so I said, 'If a major is what you
want, don't let *me* stand in your way. Go ahead and go
after him.' So she did."

A radio plays down the hall, and the wind blows in
through the window, ruffling papers on a bulletin board.
A phrase which someone has suggested and printed on
cardboard flaps gently in the breeze. "FLYING IS
HOURS AND HOURS OF BOREDOM," it says,
"BROKEN BY MOMENTS OF SHEER TERROR."

After everything has been secured, and the immediate
crisis has passed, some of the men are allowed to go home
for short periods of time, while the remainder stay on alert.
When the men are not allowed to go home, they may meet
their families at the club for dinner, and, with almost no
one in regular uniform, there is the feeling of war. If the
klaxon should grind through the dining-room loudspeaker,

the room would be emptied in an instant. There would be no time for lengthy goodbyes. And yet there is a casualness of manner that comes at such a time. Part of it is real, because the men and their families have known these times before, but part of it is pretended, and they recognize the pretence.

It is strange to see the bar unpopulated. During an alert, no one is allowed to drink, so there are empty ash trays and empty tables and a juke box that plays to an empty room. For now the beat is suspended, and then at last, it's over. Like the temperature falling in a thermometer, everything begins to let down. The ATO, the bombs, the auxiliary power units, all of them are put back where they came from. It's home again with the yard to mow and barbecued steaks for supper. All the normal things of life until it happens the next time. Or until new orders come to shake up the pattern.

In SAC such orders are inevitable. They roll around frequently. TDY (temporary duty) is another affliction common to all branches of the service but one of which SAC members get what seems more than a normal share. Under a SAC operation called "Reflex," portions of bomb wings from bases in the United States fly overseas to operate from bases in Guam, Alaska, England, North Africa, or Spain. Some wings pull more "Reflex" movements than others—depending on the wing's mission. England, Spain, and North Africa—our allies—have granted permission for SAC to maintain bases on their soil. These bases provide SAC with advance stations from which to operate.

Once they have reached the particular base to which they have been assigned, they are given quarters and alert duty begins, day and night, night and day under all conditions: the rigors of an Alaskan winter, the fever of a tropic sun. With this period of living where your ears could either freeze or fry, and, no matter what you're made of, pretty soon you're ready to go home.

Because it is inevitable that days of living under combat conditions should finally become a grind, the base often takes on the aspects of a college campus during election time. There are gags and practical jokes that would never be tolerated at home. A wad of gum in the captain's desk set produces long strings when he pulls out his pen; too many drinks at the club bar and somebody belts the daylights out of the old Jap bell standing in front; the colonel's flag, a blue and white pennant, which waves constantly and with commanding flutter from the rear bumper of his staff car, may be found anywhere from behind the bar in the officer's club to atop the colonel's own quonset, where someone has put it during the night. The colonel bears the constant thievery with something less than amiability, but realizes that it is really nothing more than a means for the men to relieve the pressure they are under.

There are bullfights near the barracks, in which a motor scooter takes the part of the bull, and somebody with more guts than brains takes the job of matador. The air police, attracted by the roaring of the motor in as unlikely a place as the barracks area, appear and close up the rings. Finally, there is the guy who catches a big, hairy land crab and puts it in the squadron commander's bed, at the sudden sight of which the major almost faints.

Bridge, poker, letters, the constant drag toward home. By the time their TDY is over, everyone is ready to leave.

For Obie, on TDY for the first time, he was ready to leave almost before he got there. He and Pat hadn't been married long, and he missed her more than he'd planned. On top of everything else, she had written telling him that he was going to be a father. He had found it difficult to adjust to the news from such a distance, but by the time he got home, he had become accustomed enough to the idea to have bought the baby a panda.

Once home, the time seemed to come with amazing speed. One morning Pat woke him and said she thought they'd better head for the hospital. Obie called a friend of his named Wightman and asked him to sign him out at the squadron. "I think Pat's going to have the baby." (He found out later that Wightman had taken care of things. The signout read: "Lt. Jas. E. Obenauf: Having a baby, maybe.)

That night about seven, David Obenauf arrived. He weighed five pounds and nine ounces, and he wasn't very pretty. After that there were night bottles and diapers, and life was not the same. Fatherhood settled in with grim finality. Now a year and a little bit later, there was going to be another one.

In the meantime, to complicate matters, David had begun to walk, and the living room looked like it had been robbed. The coffee table had been cleared of bric-a-brac and so had the end tables. The top of the TV was bald. The lamp shade was slightly crooked from having been repeatedly dumped on the floor, and the dining-room carpet had a brown spot where cereal had been poured. Still, for Obie there were compensations. He had bought David a baseball, and David was showing promise. He could wind up with a viciousness that threw his whole body out of joint. "Hey, Davie, throw it!" and pow! it would hit the wall. Pat sighed and held onto the hope that the next one would be a girl.

That was life for Obie—Pat and David and the Air Force. He was too young to have developed any serious philosophy of life, but this didn't bother him. There were a few things he despised and a few things he loved, and on these few he operated. He had no use, for example, for guys who went around getting Brownie points (apple polishers); he held in equal contempt the ones who made it their business to take care of yours. (The this-is-your-life-but-let-me-tell-you-how-to-run-it clan); and those who professed a belief in something but only stuck by whatever it was so long as the rules didn't get in their way. He believed a man should have convictions and stick by them no matter what.

The things he loved he loved deeply. He also loved selectively. He could name them all on the fingers of one hand, but if anybody thought he was going to, they were crazy. Age had not changed his reluctance to share his innermost feelings with anyone.

As for outward attributes, he was possessed of a speed and quickness which got him places a little bit faster than he or anybody else usually anticipated. His speech and thought mirrored these qualities, and the composite picture was of a guy who had been wired for slightly higher than average voltage, so that the fuses wouldn't blow out.

This extra quick movement and the clipped and telegraphic conversation made some people skeptical about his ever having a serious thought. There was also a naiveté about him that made the older ones feel that they ought to look out for him, not because he was helpless but because of his apparent utter disregard for things like life insurance and savings accounts, the solid things of life.

The truth of the matter was that although he might not have known the ins and outs of higher finance, he could, if he had to, make a dollar go farther than almost anybody. He called himself a tightwad with a kind of pride, and, sometimes in order to demonstrate it, he and a particular buddy of his would sweat each other out for an hour over a dime cup of coffee.

The aptitude he had for pranks as a boy had not left him and possibly never would. When a friend of his got married, Obie rigged the wheels of the car so that every time he turned a corner, the horn would honk. On Guam, he sickened quickly of "nothing but coconuts and rocks" and indulged himself one day by borrowing a couple of life jackets the navy had left lying around, also a gunner's helmet which caught his eye. The same day he found a loose buoy floating in near shore and rolled all two hundred pounds of it back up on the beach to his barracks. He was almost there when the AP's caught him, and it was difficult to deny anything since he had both brilliant yellow life jackets on (inflated!) and the helmet on his head. No matter what he might have been able to hide or explain, there wasn't much he could say or do about the buoy except that nobody had seemed to want it.

Pat matched him in spirit if not in outward action. The husky voice had a slow and soothing quality, and when Obie's tongue galloped, hers was often silent. It could, however, be ruinous. She had a way of cutting him down to size that even he had to appreciate.

At the moment Binbrook one-six began to come up over Dalhart, his thoughts strayed briefly to how he would change Davie's room around to accommodate the new baby, when John Cobb called him on the interphone.

# CHAPTER III

~~~~~~~~~~~~~~~~~~~~~~~~~~~~~~~~~~~~~~~~~~~~~~~~~~~~~~~~~~~~~~~~~~

"Observer to co-pilot. I'm ready for the pre-IP check list."

On the work table before John Cobb was a slender ringed notebook bound in canvas. Inside the book was page after page of lists of items to be called off before making a bomb run. Each page was sealed in a hard plastic cover, which prevented any ruffling and made the pages easy to turn.

~~~~~~~~~~~~~~~~~~~~~~~~~~~~~~~~~~~~~~~~~~~~~~~~~~~~~~~~~~~~~~~~~~

He began calling the list out, and on the heels of his words came Obie's almost simultaneous reply from an identical check-list notebook he held in his hands.

"Aerial camera.——Bomb spot."

"Camera doors.——Open."

"Off-set data.——Correct."

"Ballistics.——Measured and computed."

"True air speed.——Computed."

"Radar optical.——On."

And so on down the list in a dual count-down that put every instrument and every mechanical device connected with the run through a double check.

While few people appreciate the fact, the observer now has the most important job in the crew. The sole purpose of any flight is to successfully accomplish a mission, and no mission is accomplished unless you bomb the target accurately. In order to assure such accuracy, the observer is provided not only with months of rigorous training, but the tools of his trade; radar scope, computer, and a set of panel instruments. His work table, which fills the area in front of him, is a mass of books and papers, and his fingers must be quick with the pencil throughout the flight. He measures altitude, accomplishes wind runs, computes air speed and ballistics. Taken all together, these figures enable him to calculate how fast and just where the bomb will fall. When he has made all his calculations, he sets them into the proper instruments and puts the cross hairs on the aiming point.

A few minutes out from the target, another such list is checked off. It is called the IP check list. (IP stands for "initial point," meaning the initial point of the bomb run, at which time the observer actually starts looking for the target itself.) Immediately after this list is completed, the observer calls the pilot. "Give me second station." By this he means, "Give me control of the aircraft." From this point on, until they are actually over the target, the ship belongs to him. He is no longer merely navigator-bombardier. He is pilot as well. He puts his hand on the dead man's stick and takes the ship in.

In the meantime, the co-pilot calls the nearest ground station to see if their plane is cleared to be scored. Twenty seconds out from target, a tone switch clicks on in the ship, a steady "brrrrr," like the sound in a telephone before you begin to dial. This is the signal to the ground station that the plane is making her run. Directly over the bomb plot, the tone switch cuts off. When the "brrring" stops in the aircraft, it goes off at the station below, and an automatic pencil drops onto a piece of paper. This spot represents the place on which the bomb has theoretically dropped. By this method it is possible to compute how close a bombardier has actually come to hitting his given target, and by this method he is graded. The results of the run are reported to the aircraft and also back to the home base.

With the "bombs away" call, the observer gives the ship back to the pilot and immediately begins his post-release check list. The many switches that have been positioned for the bomb drop during the pre-IP, IP, and bomb run check lists must be repositioned to their normal configuration. Again the co-pilot calls them out to the observer, who checks them as he goes.

"Aerial camera.——Off."

"Camera doors.——Closed."

"Radar optical.——Off."

When he has finished the list, he picks up his computer and begins to get ready for the next run.

"Calculus on a roller coaster" is what the observer's job has been called, a job which makes him the busiest man in the crew. From the time a ship leaves the ground until it puts back down eight to ten hours later, work is constant. He never has time to eat, smoke, or think, about anything, that is, but the mission.

All this takes place in a little metal tomb in the nose of the ship. High above the observer's head on either side of the nose there are two small squares paned with plexiglass,

but even this limited amount of light is usually c
means of a curtain. In the day of the space age it s...... ....-
portant that the man whose purpose it is to guide the ship
and bomb the target be completely blind. All he sees is
what he sees in his radar scope, and that nothing more than
hundreds of miles of pattern, colorless, devoid of struc-
ture, like the negative of a photograph or a relief map in
which mountains appear as splotchy high spots and cities
irregular flaky patches. It is image rather than form, and
to the uninitiated, the task of spotting a particular mass in
a scope littered with masses appears to be completely impossible.

To the uninitiated it is, which is where the training
comes in. By the time a man finishes his course, he has
learned not merely to put the cross hairs on Denver and
blast it to kingdom come, but to put the cross hairs on the
west wall of a factory site in Denver and bring the west
wall down. "Pin point accuracy" means exactly that, and
a topnotch observer makes it his business to hit the pin.

If the work is constant, it, like everything else in life,
contains the seeds of its own blessing, for if Cobb had had
time to think about where he was and how many hours he
spent there, he could not have stood it. For a man who
had always loved the out-of-doors the way he did, oblitera-

tion of everything relating to normal sight, smell, and sound would finally have driven him crazy.

As a child he had lived in Elko, Nevada, which lies at the feet of the Ruby mountains. The earliest memory he had of anything was the snow on their peaks. The earliest sound he could remember was the call of the coyotes just after dark; the earliest smell (and the one he still loved best) was that of the sage brush after rain. He lived in the city of Elko with his grandparents, but he often felt that the mountains were his home.

As a youngster, when he first began to climb them his grandmother had complained. "You're going to get killed someday." It was no use trying to reassure her. There was nothing he could say, besides which there was the bald bare fact that at least on one occasion she had almost been right.

The day it happened, he and his dog Zon had been out since morning. It was early spring, but the ground was still covered with snow, and the snow with a thin sheet of ice. The climbing was hard and wearing, and about noon they stopped to rest. Zon sat beside him, her breath steaming the air, and together they watched a storm cloud coming up in the distance. But in the mountains sight is deceiving, and suddenly it was over them boiling in over the peak top. In the swiftly encroaching darkness, he turned to look at Zon. Every hair on her back stood straight up, and his own scalp began to prickle. It was the first sign that lightning was going to strike. Not just somewhere, sometime, but right on that spot.

"Zon!" he called to her and pitched himself forward. The pair of them slipped and slid down to a snow bank a hundred and thirty feet below. Immediately after, wham! The lightning struck above them dancing on the cliff points. He crouched beside Zon in the darkness and, after the initial shock was over, took delight in being that close to the violent and elemental forces of nature.

He never told his grandmother about it. She worried enough, and, while the actual stroke of lightning had scared the wits out of him, it didn't cure him of climbing. Nothing ever would. Irresistably attracted, he climbed throughout his boyhood until he became a man. Only then was he able to know what the attraction was. Some books said it was getting to the top, but these books were wrong. It was not mastering the mountain; it was mastering yourself. It was making yourself do something you were afraid to do. Sometimes balanced precariously on a minute rock projection, there was a blinding moment of fear when you wanted never to move. What you did at that moment was to conquer yourself, which was the most important thing a man ever had to do.

This wasn't for a kid to know, but he knew a lot of things about himself now he hadn't known then, many of them thanks to his mother who had kept a book about him from the time he was born to his seventh year; pictures, facts, and stories that revealed him to himself.

"Today John was two. He celebrated the occasion by letting the birds out of the cage. When I asked him why, he said, 'Because they wanted to go.'" (Even now at twenty-four he cannot stand to see creatures caged.)

"John has a sense of humor. The other day Mother asked him what he was going to do when he'd sucked all his thumb off. He said he had lots of fingers."

"This is a picture of John's father. I want him to remember what he looked like."

If it hadn't been for the photograph, John's only memory of his father would have been a blurred one of a big man on a couch; of a doctor who came and an ambulance in which they took his father away. The doctor had reassured—John—"He's going to be all right."—but his father had died.

After that he grieved a child's grief, hiding his head under the covers, but, fortunately for him, there was someone to take his father's place. It was his Uncle Archie, who was his mother's brother. Archie owned a gasoline truck, and he had a particular fondness for John. Even when John was very small, Arch used to come and take him for rides in the truck. They rode out in the hills beyond Elko, delivering gasoline to the ranchers. This was a lot of fun for John, still the greater part of his life had to be spent with his grandparents, since his mother had gone to work in Reno to help support him and his two younger brothers. He loved both his grandparents, but in the household of the Lanis, discipline was old-fashioned and strict. It seldom took the form of physical punishment, being limited to the verbal, but the words were strong ones. John had a perfect cursing vocabulary by the time he was three, inherited from his grandpa, who was second to none.

There was one exception to this form of verbal punishment, however, and it also belonged to his grandpa. Grandpa used to sit in the living room listening to the radio or reading. He always wore carpet slippers, and if John misbehaved, Grandpa would take one of them off and smack him. By the time John was six, however, he found that he was quicker than his grandfather, and when he saw the old man take off his shoe, he would make a dive for the kitchen. But Grandpa had an ace in the hole even youth was unable to beat. Grandpa had been pitcher on a local softball team and, though the years had mellowed him otherwise, it had not mellowed his aim. With devastating accuracy, the slipper always caught John in the small of the back with a solid whap! just as he turned the corner.

Later punishments were left to Archie. Arch's punishment was also verbal, but it took the form of derision, and John soon found that there was nothing worse than being made to feel like a fool in front of Arch. He was fifteen when he got his first full dose of it, and he never forgot it.

It was at John's own insistence that he had been allowed to take the gasoline truck on a delivery all by himself. The truck was big and unwieldly, but he had driven it before with Arch, and he didn't see why he couldn't drive it alone even if it was up in the mountains. Persuaded finally by constant badgering, Arch let him go.

Everything went fine on the way up, but coming back, a bee flew in the cab. John took his eyes off the road long enough to swat it, and the next thing he knew he was in trouble. The big truck hit the shoulder of a curve, and he felt the shoulder give. It crumbled and slowly gave, as if a big foot had pushed it down.

There was a breathless moment, and then over she turned. Bang! Bang! Bang! Bang! John counted four times. It ended up on its wheels, with John miraculously unhurt. He reached out and opened the cab door and, looking up, saw the road high above him. He knew nobody had seen him come down, so there was nothing to do but make his way back up and walk until he found the nearest ranch house.

When he got back up on the roadway, he looked ahead of him. There, not twenty feet from the spot where he had gone off, the drop was absolutely sheer. If he had gone off there, he would surely have been killed. But he wasn't thinking about the drop really. He was thinking about Arch. He had to tell him, and what was Arch going to say?

He thought about it all the way to the ranch house, and by the time he got there, he wished he had been killed. Then Arch could have looked down with tears in his eyes and said, "That was my favorite nephew." As it was, Arch said plenty, but he didn't say that.

That year he was a Junior in high school, busy with football and girls. The next year he was a Senior and got his third football letter. Only one semester did he make the honor roll, but that didn't particularly matter. What he liked (Math and History), he put his mind to, and those grades were good. What he did not like (English and Civics), he did not put his mind to, and those grades were bad. Still, when he took the college entrance examinations, he came out third in a class of fifty. Arch was called in by the principal and told John should go to college.

College had not been part of John Cobb's plan. He already knew what he wanted to do. He wanted to join the

Air Force. When it was that he first decided he wanted to fly, he was not certain. Maybe long before he realized. His mother's book said he'd seen his first airplane when he was just a year old. He had screamed with delight when it took off and cried when it didn't come back. A month later they passed the airport, and he stood on his toes and yelled. They had to stop the car and let him watch until the planes took off.

Or maybe it had begun with Arch. Arch was in World War II and flew a B-17. While he was in England, he wrote John lots of letters. The letters and plunking out "Let's Remember Pearl Harbor" on the piano with his Aunt June was the closest John came to that war, but it left an impression, and he knew he wanted to fly. He went to the University of Nevada in Reno one year, and then, with Archie's permission, he quit and enlisted.

He applied for pilot training, but he hadn't had the two years of college required, so they made him a navigator-bombardier, which didn't set too well. Still, they told him he could apply for pilot training after he'd been in a while, and he had to let that suffice.

It was while he was in Sacramento finishing up his training that he met an old friend from Elko. It was Cherie Charlebois and her mother, and Mrs. Charlebois invited him out to dinner. After the first time, he went to see her often, and, by the time he graduated, he and Cherie were in love. They both decided they wanted to get married back home in Nevada, so they took Cherie's mother and father with them and headed for Reno.

While John was waiting for Cherie and her mother to do some last-minute shopping, he went into a bar. He didn't think he was nervous, but suddenly it hit him: a cramp under his left rib so hard he could hardly breathe. He ordered a shot of Jack Daniels. Then he ordered another. The pain began to go. By the time he'd had the third one, he was ready for the wedding. In the meantime, he'd developed a certain kinship with Adam. When God took that rib to make Eve with, John knew it had hurt.

They were married in Trinity Episcopal Church in Reno and had a honeymoon on the way to Dyess Air Force Base, where John had been given his first assignment. Since Dyess was not yet heavily populated, they were fortunate enough to get quarters on the base. It was here at Dyess that their first baby, David, was born. He was just a year old now, and there was another on the way.

Since Cherie was nuts about kids, they'd probably have a dozen. Somehow he'd been lucky enough to have found the right woman. Calm, unexcitable, she was amazingly understanding, and their interests were the same. She loved reading and listening to music ("brave music" he called it, like Wagner and Shostakovitch), and she loved camping out as much as he did. They went as often as they could, and even now, six months pregnant, it never seemed to bother her that she had to sleep in a sleeping bag rather than a real bed; that she had to cook on a one burner Coleman rather than a gas stove, and that sometimes she got darn cold. She didn't mind running after the baby to keep him from falling off cliffs, and she didn't mind the dog and the cat that always went with them. (Also, there was always a box on the floor of the car containing Tuscarora's perpetual kittens.) She never complained about being uncomfortable with all this jammed in a Fiat, and, if fellow travelers along the highway stared at the dog's head out one window and the baby's out the other with the cat chinning for space beneath, Cherie merely stared back.

A man, even a man with a temper, could live with a woman like that. As a matter of fact, her self-possession seemed to have rubbed off on him. He no longer went into rages the way he had when he was younger. Home had a peace about it he found no other place; books and talk and music and his favorite pipe.

He could feel the pipe now in his pocket as he leaned over the scope. It was the same one he'd lost up in the mountains one day when he made a delivery for Arch. Just before he went into the service, he had taken the truck out for a delivery in the mountains, and, by the time he got to the ranch house, it had begun to snow. When he got out of the truck, he dropped the pipe, although he didn't know it at the time. He only missed it later when it was too late to go back. He regretted the loss of the pipe because it was his favorite, but he made do with second best. Then one day three years later when he was home on leave, he made another trip for Arch. It was to the same ranch house in the springtime, and, when he got out of the truck and looked down, there was the pipe.

He was not one given to lucky pieces or tokens, but he had a particular feeling about that pipe, and he always carried it with him, although there was rarely time to smoke it. Tonight was no exception. There'd be no smoking for him.

He had finished making his bomb run on Dalhart and was getting set to measure altitude for a bomb run on Denver when Jim Graves made an announcement.

# CHAPTER IV

"Drop in oil pressure on number three engine."

Jim's eyes caught the needle as it made a slow descent. He reached out and pushed number three throttle forward. Slowly the needle rose.

"Checks out within limits, but if it drops again I'm going to cut it."

There are six engines on the B-47, which leaves five to take care of the failure of any one. As far as getting back was concerned, there was no worry about that. What bothered Jim was the possibility of an engine fire. He would have to watch it.

He moved in his ejection seat trying to stretch his legs. Six feet four inches didn't make for comfort, but then when had it? Everything was too short. Beds and pants and people and, when he was growing up, the kids had always called him "Legs." On top of that somebody had always wanted to fight him to prove they could lick the biggest. The playground at recess was a series of minor skirmishes which usually ended in a split lip for somebody.

Jim had inherited the height from his Grandfather Wood, who had stood six feet three and, according to the stories, Mr. Wood used the height to good advantage in the days when he was a driver on the Chisholm Trail. When at last he tired of trail driving, he bought a spot of ground that had caught his eye and settled down to farming near the little town of Joshua out a ways from Fort Worth. When each of his four children grew up and married, he gave each of them a hundred acres of the four hundred he had bought. It was therefore on his mother's wedding present that Jim was born and grew up.

Growing up on a farm is always much the same. It doesn't matter who the boy is or what the particular place. There are cows to milk and fields to plow and crops to be sown and harvested. If there was anything different about Jim's own farm background, it lay in his father's methods.

Mr. Graves was a hard-working man, but he never worked uselessly. He had long since found that he could make the farm pay without breaking everyone's back; that he got just about as good a yield on his cotton without hoeing it every day, and he figured his back and his son's backs were worth more than an extra bale of cotton. So it was that Jim and his dad often had more time than other farmers to do the things they liked. Hot August days when the sun beat down, his father would turn to him and say, "Let's knock off and go make some ice cream," or "We haven't been fishing since the last time. Let's go down on the river."

All in all, Jim's childhood was a time of no pressures and few worries; a time when one day simply followed another in unvarying pattern. The slight demarkation along the way to manhood went almost unnoticed. Only now from his vantage point of thirty-five years could he see that here and here and here something special had happened to make him the person he was.

He could remember, for example, when it was that he had eased over the ledge of boyhood and stood (he thought) as a man. He was nine years old, and it was the day his mother let him quit wearing long stockings. At that time it was the custom for a boy to wear short pants, and, in order to keep the exposed part of the leg protected, they wore long, knee-length hose. Jim had always hated the stockings. They would not stay up. Running, riding, walking, they worked slowly down until they hung about his ankles in a crumpled head. He was continually having to stoop over to pull them up. On the day when he wore his first long pants, it was not the pants but the ankle-length socks that registered his coming to manhood.

The minor humiliations of childhood (which seemed so major at the time) came back with equal clarity. There was the time, for instance, when he got his first whipping. Not with a fly swatter the way his mother had always punished him, but by his father with his father's belt. He did not suppose that in the whole of his childhood he had ever really gotten what might be called a "licking." Lickings implied black and blue marks and considerable physical pain. Even when his father was most angry, he never whipped him like that. Still Jim knew what it felt like to have welts on his legs, and one day, rather than stand and take it, he simply took off.

There was as much surprise as fear in the sudden flight. It was not like him to defy his father, but having made his move, ten-year-old pride demanded that he stick to his guns. He heard his father call after him, "It's getting on to dark. It will be cold out there soon. You'd better come on back." But he didn't pay any attention. He headed for the pasture, and soon the moon came out. It coated the fields with a white chill, and the barn stood big and black. It was cold and he was hungry, but he would not give up.

Later he circled up near the house where he could see a lamp burning. His mother was in the kitchen. She was getting supper, and he could see the big steaming bowls. His stomach stirred and complained. Later the light moved into the living room. They would be sitting around the fire, his brother and sister doing homework, his mother and father talking.

He thought about sleeping out in the barn, but he didn't really want to. He was shivering now, and the goose bumps were almost as big as he was. Finally he couldn't stand it any longer. He went up to the back porch; he eased open the screen door, trying to keep it from squeaking, and he saw old Blackie lying back in a corner curled up on his blanket. Blackie looked warm and comfortable. Jim pushed in beside him. He lay there thinking he'd found the solution, and then the fleas began to bite. He scratched and turned and twisted and finally gave up. Flea-bitten and half-frozen he went inside. His dad got the belt down and whipped him the way Jim had known he would.

But there were warmer memories: school dances, and

football games, and pretty girls. He was often the leader in a ground play which involved catching the girls in the cloakroom and kissing them. The other guys could scoff if they wanted to about girls and how silly they were, but right from the first he saw they had possibilities.

The year he was a Senior in high school, things became more serious, however. World War II broke out, and he watched the headlines anxiously, afraid it would all be over before he could graduate and enlist. But there was plenty of action for Jim to see when the time came for him to see it. He joined the Air Corps in 1942, when he was barely eighteen.

The Air Corps was an accident. He'd meant to be a Marine, but the day he went in to Fort Worth to get his enlistment papers he passed a sign in the hall. There was a picture on it of a man in a cockpit and the words beneath it read "GLIDER TRAINING." Instead of going to the left and the Marine office, he peeled off to the right.

He was accepted, took his training, and was ready for his commission. Then a colonel put in an appearance and said the whole thing was off. The glider program hadn't worked out, and they were shifting all the trainees. They had a choice of applying as cadets for pilot training or becoming part of a ground crew. Jim applied for cadets, got his Wings, and one morning in November, 1944, climbed into a B-17 and took off for England.

The afternoon they landed, Jim Graves and his squadron buddies stood watching a bomb group come in. They had been out over Europe, and now they were drifting back. One by one eighteen planes droned in, heavy, lurching, shot up. Thirty-six had taken off. The Germans had cut them in half. Looking at them, Jim realized that when he went he wouldn't come back. The knowledge did not frighten him. He simply knew it was so.

But Jim's moment of premonition proved to be inaccurate. A month later, when he pulled his first mission, he did come back. He came back five or six times, and then he knew he was going to live. With a sudden burst of reassurance, he wanted to go where the fighting was hottest. This meant Berlin.

He had a fight with a captain who said that Jim was crazy to want to go. Jim stuck his fist out and knocked the captain into a stove. He had never liked him anyway, because a couple of times he had caught him being rude to the enlisted men, so this seemed as good an excuse as any Jim was likely to find for hitting him. There was a little session in the CO's office afterward, but nothing ever came of it. Turned out the CO didn't like the captain any better than Jim did.

After the incident, Jim asked to go to Berlin and they let him. The morning they took off from England the sky was black with planes. They droned out over the channel, wave after wave after wave, and, after about four hours, they were over their target. They were flying in two group formations with a wide alley between; enough space between the groups to prevent any collision. Then, according to the flight plan, they began to turn directly into each other in a V-shaped pattern. Only after bombs away did both of the groups turn away from one another.

Even with the direct, V-shaped maneuver, there was room enough to prevent the ships coming into contact with one another except in Jim's case. He was flying tail-end Charlie. This meant that he was the last plane in his group, and, because the distance between the two groups had completely played out by the time it was Jim's turn to peel off, his plane drifted through the last ships of the other group.

It looked like he would make it all right, and then he hit their prop wash. The heavy turbulence flipped him over, and his plane was on its back. He knew that they were falling. He didn't think he could bring her back over. Then, when the altimeter stood at twelve thousand, he righted her somehow. But at that altitude they were a prime target for flak. It was coming up all around them.

He could hear the explosions and see the red centers in their cores as they burst. In a constant hard staccato, the flak smashed into the fuselage. He pushed up the throttles and began to climb. F-51's came in to protect him, and he headed for the channel.

When they landed in England, they counted 248 holes. They were literally riddled, and yet not one man in his crew had been injured. They began to call him Lucky Graves.

The next trip was over Dresden, and that time his luck almost played out. The plane flying just ahead of him dropped its bombs on the plane below. The plane that was hit splintered and burst upward and parts of it were thrown into Jim's ship. It knocked out two of his engines and part of a third. In the plane that had been hit he could hear the pilot saying, "Bail out! Bail out! Bail out!" There was time enough for the bail out, but for some reason nobody did. Suddenly, the plane burst into flames, and Jim watched it go down.

But there wasn't time to think about it. His ship was shot up bad. He knew they couldn't possibly make it back to England, but he thought they might make it back to France. At the final briefing before they left England, they had been given the Allied lines. "Patton has cut in this far. If you have to make an emergency landing, try to come down here."

He didn't think he could make it. All he could do was try. They lumbered along getting lower, and he could see the tops of houses. At that altitude the ground forces could have hit them with anything. Even rocks would have hurt. He was about to give the bail-out order when suddenly he heard the navigator. "Runway! Runway dead ahead!"

He put the lurching and stumbling plane down. As they hurtled down the runway, he still didn't know whether it was an Allied or German air strip. When the ship stopped rolling, men came swarming out. With a sigh of relief Jim Graves saw they wore the uniform of the U.S. Air Corp. They told him, however, that if he had been a few hours earlier, the fellows who greeted him would have belonged to der Führer. Patton had come in twenty miles that day, and those twenty miles had saved them.

For a man who loved excitement this life was the berries. He never worried about anything; he simply lived it up. When he had completed thirty-five missions, he was slated to go home, but he couldn't bear to leave while it was still going on, so he signed on for another tour. But by that time Hitler had had enough. When he went up in smoke at Berlin, Jim started home. The U.S.S. Brazil took him, and he had never been so sick in his life; next time he crossed the ocean he vowed he'd do it in a plane.

He decided to stay in the service a while, but it didn't work out. He was ferrying B-17's to the graveyard, and he didn't like it. They sat row after row after row in ignominious retirement; the ships which had done so much toward winning the war had been put out to pasture, and nothing was the same.

With enough points and then some to support him, he got out and went to college. He was working on his prelaw at Texas Christian University in Fort Worth when the Berlin Airlift started. He thought there was going to be another war, and the old excitement began to build up.

If it hadn't been for Enel, going back in would have been easy, but now there was Enel, and it was going to be hard to leave her. He had met her at T.C.U. and she was awfully pretty. Small-boned, black-haired, always pin neat, she had been a model at some of the leading stores in Dallas. They'd planned to get married just as soon as he finished school, but the idea of Berlin kept eating away at him. He talked it over finally with a lawyer friend in Fort Worth. Should he go back in or should he stay out and get his law degree?

The friend advised him to go back in. Financially, he told Jim, no young lawyer could make the money Jim

would make. It was a long hard grind, and Jim loved flying so much that the lawyer thought it was the thing for
Jim to do. So, a year short of graduation, Jim quit T.C.U.
He told Enel, of course, before he did it, and she agreed
it was probably best.

They packed him off to Montana for a few months of
C-54 transition training, and it was while he was there
that he decided that before he went to Germany he wanted
to marry Enel. He put in a long distance phone call and
asked her to come. She came a few days later and they
were married.

There was only one bad minute. It happened during the
wedding ceremony. The minister asked Enel if she took
Jim to be her lawful wedded husband, and Enel found
that her vocal cords had become paralyzed. Jim looked
at her finally and said, "Well, honey, tell the man."

They were together a week. A week was a very short
time, and even the promise of excitement didn't help very
much. Maybe that was why, once he got to Germany,
things were not the same. Whatever it was, it was not like
the old days when every day was a war. Flying into
Tempelhof got to be a grind. You picked her up and you
put her down, two hours both ways, two trips a day. You
carted flour, milk, vegetables, everything necessary for a
city to survive, and you were doing a vital job, but the

old excitement was missing. There was no flak flying up at him this time; no sense of real urgency. The only interesting thing that happened the whole time he was there was the trip he made into Berlin with Lindbergh as a passenger. The colonel, however, proved to be highly uncommunicative. He stood between Jim and the pilot, and he made only one remark. Jim said, "Sir, there has certainly been very little publicity connected with your visit here," and Lindbergh said, "I think I have had all the publicity in one lifetime that I need."

After six months Jim was ready to go home. In the meantime, he had made a decision. He wanted to stay in the Air Force. Enel had been indoctrinated. She knew what to expect, and he didn't think she would mind. He waited until he got back to tell her, but it was as he had thought, and Enel agreed.

But things were somehow different. He and Enel had been together so little since their marriage that they were strangers to one another. Feeling hurt and helpless, they didn't know what to do. Then along came Korea, and they thought that might be the solution. Jim would go to Korea, and they would see how things worked out.

This time Jim was away for a year. He was based at Okinawa, two hours flying time up to the 38th parallel, beyond which they did their bombing. He bombed Seoul and Wonsan and Sinuyi, but this war wasn't like the last one. Nobody seemed to be certain of exactly what they were fighting for, and the old fever just wasn't there. Or maybe it was Jim that was different. Whichever it was, when the time came, he was glad to be going home because he'd made a decision: he wanted to stay married. So, he was glad to find out, did Enel. That was all six years ago, but it seemed much longer. They had had the baby since then. He had brown eyes and dark hair, and Jim knew without parental conceit, that he was a handsome child. He might have chosen a better time to be born, still Jim had the greatest confidence in the future. It was his belief that we would fight another war but that we would win it. He had fought the last one as a young man, barely twenty and commanding his own crew. This was pretty heady stuff for a youngster, and he had fought the war accordingly. Now he was fifteen years older, and he would fight the next one differently.

There were weapons for the belly of his ship with more destructive power than the one which had blown Hiroshima to bits. There was a weapon like it for every B-47 in SAC. He never forgot this; he never took it for granted. He was old enough to know what it meant and to be concerned with its consequences. Still, given the job of dropping that bomb where it would do the most good, he would willingly give his life.

His eyes flicked to his instrument panel for another look at the number three engine. The oil pressure was barely holding. He was thinking about cutting it when Joe Maxwell spoke.

# CHAPTER V

"Aircraft Commander, this is fourth man. I'm going off oxygen to eat my flight lunch."

Joe was pretty hungry. Now he had about fifteen minutes while Cobb was measuring altitude and getting set for his bomb run on Denver. It was a relief to unfasten his oxygen mask and lean back in his seat. Not that the chair was much comfort, but he didn't think about that. He had been in the Air Force fifteen years, and you didn't think about comfort. You just did a job as best you could and didn't ask for favors.

For Joe this came easier than it might have for some. He was not accustomed to favors; life had not been easy. His father had been a Chief Petty Officer in the Navy when Joe was growing up, and, whereas there had always been a certain monetary security, there had also been a corresponding insecurity stemming from the fact, perhaps, that his father was away at sea most of the time. This meant that there was no strong parental hand at the wheel. There was also the feeling that home was not really home. They didn't move often, but they were at the constant whim of the Navy, and there was always the certainty that sooner or later they would move.

The first home Joe remembered was on the Naval Base on the island of St. Thomas in the West Indies. Memories of the place still lingered; the enormous barracks, the heavy anchor chains linking the white-graveled walks, the long piers, the blue-gray ships, and their big white house. He remembered a housekeeper named Marie, who was black as ink and spoke French; Mardi Gras, when the natives danced and sang, and men walked on big high stilts. Finally there was clearest of all the memories, the one of the night when the hurricane came, and they took shelter in the Navy barracks. For some reason there was stamped indelibly on his mind the fact that he had sat at a long plank table eating Post Toasties.

Back home afterward, they found that the storm had piled up the boat his father had built to take the family around the islands. It was in pretty bad shape, but his father fixed it the way he always fixed things; immediately and emphatically. He was a powerful man, harsh, driven by something that at that age, Joe was too young to understand. Only now could Joe look back and see what had made his father the way he was, and that only because Joe himself had become somewhat like him in his later years.

If his father was as much like himself as Joe imagined, then he knew that his dad had been goaded by a feeling of insecurity which made him rush at whatever there was to be done as if there were no time to do it tomorrow. Whatever Joe did now, he did with that same passion, one that bordered on self-punishment. It was not only the way he worked, it was the way he played. Hunting, fishing, playing poker, he played too hard. And, strangest of all, it was not the winning that mattered. It was simply an obsession to squeeze the particular situation dry of whatever possibilities were in it. What it boiled down to was that Joe had become a perfectionist, and perfectionists never rested easy.

This was bad and Joe knew it. He was trying to overcome it. He was glad that at least he had become aware of it, because in the awareness lay the cure. In the meantime, it would have been better perhaps, if he had held onto some of the characteristics he had had as a child; those inherited from his mother, who was as much the opposite of his father in temperament as it was possible to be. Emotional and sentimental, she preferred living in the past or the future rather than the too difficult present. The pressures and practicalities of daily living were too much for her, and she took refuge in daydreams and occasional poetry, which she wrote rather well. As a result of such a disposition, she was no disciplinarian, and, with Joe's father at sea for long periods of time, the task of keeping the four smallest Maxwells in line usually fell to his older sister, Mary.

Pete, his brother, was the oldest in the family, but Pete was so absorbed in his own activities that he paid little attention to the small fry, so it was left to Mary, the second oldest, to keep Frank and Joe and the two younger sisters, Alice and Betty, in line. Joe looked back now half-amused, half-amazed at the problems which Mary must have endured in her younger years.

When Joe was four, his father was transferred from the West Indies to Norfolk, Virginia. It was here that Joe started to school in a highly unconventional manner.

When Mary and Frank started to school, Joe wanted to

go too. He was only five, but he felt that being left at home with "the babies" was sissy and unfair, so he tagged along with Mary and Frank to the parochial school they attended. He went so often and with such persistence that the Sister finally gave him a seat. Thus, by weight of habitual presence, Joe infiltrated first grade.

During this period of his life, they lived both in Portsmouth and Norfolk, and, looking back on that time, he was again conscious of shift and change, the underlying insecurity. His dad retired from the Navy the first time at the height of the depression in 1934. This made it hard on the family since retirement pay was not high. As a result, from the time Joe was old enough, he began to earn his own money.

The first cash he ever dragged in was from the sale of whiskey bottles. There was an old negro couple near Portsmouth who had a still. They paid two cents for every empty bottle, and the bottles were plentiful since, during prohibition, they could be found on almost any vacant lot. As a side line to old whiskey bottles or soft-drink bottles, Joe sold bunches of wild flowers. He gathered jonquils in the country meadows not far from his house and took them into town to sell. A good healthy bunch of jonquils brought ten cents. When you added this to whiskey bottles, you sometimes had a dollar.

Other methods of earning money were more conventional. Lemonade stands in the summer, mowing lawns, caddying on the weekends, and, when he was ten, a paper route.

The paper route he would never forget since it cost him a chunk of his conscience. He bought the route for five dollars from the boy who had it. Five dollars was a lot of money; a lot more than Joe had, so he promised Alvin he would pay him just as soon as he got it. For some reason Alvin didn't hound him, and Joe didn't go looking for Al. As a result, the debt remained unpaid. At the time, Joe didn't worry about it, but he worried plenty later. Every time he thought about that paper route, he felt a twinge of conscience. It ate at him for ten years, and then one day, through the most casual chance, he was able to repay it.

He was on a bus going from Dallas to Fort Worth, and there, sitting across the aisle from him, was Al. Joe took five dollars out of his pocket and handed it to him. When Al pocketed the money, Joe never felt so good in his life.

He graduated from the paper route to an ice cream parlor. It was hard, working and going to school too, squeezing the homework in between ice cream cones, but by this time, life had become a perpetual juggling act, and anything else would have seemed unreal. His mother and father had separated in 1940, and so it was all the more up to him to earn what he could.

As a fill-in job, he sold newspapers whenever they needed extra help. He hawked them in the streets of Portsmouth on the day Germany attacked Poland. "GERMANY WARS ON POLAND." The headlines were big and black. He was only fifteen at the time, but he was afraid of what it meant. His worst fears were realized when the United States entered the war. After that, he watched the ships in grim procession go out of the Norfolk harbor. They sailed sleek, taut, and trim, and they returned black and blasted and charred. Oil coated the Virginia beaches, and an occasional ship blew up in sight of the shore. It was a gray time for his country, and Joe, who always took things with conscience, was pretty concerned about it.

He graduated from high school in 1942, but, having gotten an early start in grade school, he wasn't old enough to join up. To fill in the year before he was eighteen, he got a job at the Naval Air Station at Norfolk. During that time, he thought about the branch of service he'd like to join.

He wanted to join the Air Corps, but he didn't think he had the qualifications. Then one day he saw some young guys get out of some Navy fighters, and he said to himself, "If they can do it, I can." Six months later he joined the Air Corps.

This was the beginning of a time for Joe he would never forget. For the first time in a long while he was free of responsibilities. Uncle Sam was sending him to college. He was sent to the University of Alabama to take courses in navigation and, in spite of the war, college was still college. There were school dances and lots of pretty girls. He was tall, and there was something about a uniform even if it wasn't dragging down but $35.00 a month.

Weekends he went with his buddies into Birmingham in an old rented car they called a "pusher." (She couldn't be relied upon to go under her own steam. You were liable to have to push 'er.) Occasionally they bought rum from the civilians who had to take a fifth of it in order to buy honest-to-gosh liquor, and they made the town.

There was an underlying element of deep seriousness, however, behind all the larking. If he wanted to get his commission (and he did, more than he'd ever wanted anything), then he had to make his grades. So he hit the books constantly and conscientiously, and, in the end, the study paid off. He got his navigator's wings and orders to report to Saipan. But about that time the U.S. let go an atomic bomb over Hiroshima, and that was the end of the war.

A lot of guys were sorry because they hadn't gotten to

do any fighting, but Joe felt differently about it. Peace was more important, and he was glad it was over. Now he had only one thing in mind; get out and go to college. He had to wait until he had enough points, however, and he waited it out in Fort Worth.

While he was stationed at Carswell Air Force Base, he met a girl named Doe. He told his roommate later she was the most beautiful girl he'd ever seen in his life. Joe took her out three times, and after the third time he knew he wanted to marry her. He felt this was probably too quick for Doe however so he put off asking her until he got back from a cross-country trip. He was gone for two weeks, and, by the time he got back, Doe was ready to say "yes."

He spent the whole morning before the wedding working on an old Chevrolet. He had bought it for four hundred dollars (borrowed at that!). It was a 1934 model, and it had four wheels and a top, which was about all you could say for it except that the wheels had tires. The tires were shot, but Joe thought he could fix them. The only thing was that, before he could get one fixed, another one would blow out. He spent the whole day going from one wheel to another in what seemed an endless succession of explosions. He barely made the wedding that night at eight o'clock.

They took the car seven hundred and fifty miles to Virginia, and they really had their hands full. It rained all the way through Tennessee, both inside the car and out. The top was like a sieve, and they had to wear their raincoats all the time to keep dry. Being wet was bad enough, but as they worked their way up through the Smokies, they had a wreck that nearly finished them.

It was raining, and Doe was sitting next to him asleep. A car coming up over a mountain momentarily blinded Joe with its headlights. He applied his brakes, they skidded, and over they went. They turned over twice and would probably have kept on turning if they hadn't got hung up in some trees. He and Doe fumbled around in the darkness and finally pulled themselves out. Miraculously, there were no bones broken, and the car wasn't even hurt much. They got a wrecker to come pull it back up the mountain and left Tennessee the next morning with nothing more to show for it than a black eye for Doe.

But if the wreck had spared them physically, it had demolished their pocketbook. Part of their precious honeymoon money had gone to pay for the wrecker, so they stumbled into North Carolina stretching their last dollar out on scrambled eggs without bacon. If it hadn't been for Joe's brother at Fort Bragg, they wouldn't have had any lunch. As it was, Frank had just gotten his mustering-out pay, so Joe and Doe had steaks and gassed the Chevrolet.

In Virginia finally, they spent part of their leave with his mother and part of it with his dad, and Doe got to meet as many of his brothers and sisters as time and circumstance allowed.

When they got back to Fort Worth after the leave was over, Joe got orders to report to Japan. This came as a blow. He and Doe had only been married a few weeks, and at that time, it was impossible for wives to accompany husbands on foreign duty. They had to wait their turn to join them, sometimes as long as a year or more. Still there was nothing else for it, so Joe packed his clothes and headed for Kyushu.

He tried not to think about Doe since thinking wasn't much use, and he was partially successful. He was assigned to a group making detailed aerial photographs of all the islands of Japan. He was not only busy, he was fascinated. They flew light planes, two men to a ship, and they landed at lots of out-of-the-way places he would not otherwise have seen. As a result, he got a close look at the people, and what he saw amazed him.

They were beaten, bombed, blasted; everything was in ruin, but they had a dignity about them nothing had been able to wreck. Obedience to circumstance was a national characteristic, and they adjusted to their conquerors with a gentleness devoid of obsequiousness. For them it was dignified destitution; for Joe, a lesson in pride.

While he was there, he bought a very old ivory carving. It was of a rice farmer with long hair and a beard. He stood in a loose robe and sandals, and he was holding a sheaf of rice. The ivory had darkened and stained and cracked, but the old man stood there with that look Joe had seen so often on the faces of the people around him. It was the look of time; so patient, so eternal that he would never forget it.

Off hours he spent with his buddies of the Kyushu detachment, sight-seeing or lounging around the club bar. They sold Suntory whiskey for fifteen cents a shot, and the morning after, you knew they had issued a headache with every round. (No charge for the headache.) The stuff could not have been more than a month old, but it didn't seem half bad after the club had exhausted its nightly ration of a few bottles of American whiskey. All in all, he would have been hard put to it to find another group as congenial as the one on Kyushu. Because of them, the eighteen months before Doe came did not seem so long.

After she got there, they had a year, seeing everything there was to see, and during that time Joe made a decision. He decided he wanted to stay in the Air Force. He would have liked to go to college, but on the other hand, he had three and a half years invested in the Air Force, and he felt that he stood a pretty good chance of making that investment pay off. What was more, the Air Force presented a challenge. If he worked hard enough, he knew he could make the top of the heap, and fly with the best crews. For him, this was a worth-while goal.

Having made his decision, he began to study. During the next five years he burned a lot of midnight oil, and, at the end of that time, he was assigned to check out the 9th Recon-Wings' first B-36 on her maiden flight. For this occasion, he was sent back to Fort Worth, where he took his indoctrination at Carswell. After two weeks of class-work, finding out what the big ship was all about, he and the crew of fourteen tackled the real thing.

The crew met on two successive mornings to try and get her off the ground, but there was so much pre-flight work to be done to her that they never cranked up the engines. On the third morning things looked good for a take-off but by noon Joe had a toothache. When the doctor took a look at it, he hauled Joe off to the hospital despite his protestations.

That night Joe was lying in his hospital bed, still fuming at having missed the take-off, when they came and told him that the B-36 had crashed on the take-off. Three of her propellers had reversed on the take-off, and four of her crew had been killed. The four that died were all in Joe's compartment. If it hadn't been for the toothache, Joe would have been dead.

This was a shock, although death was not new to Joe. One after another during the years he'd been flying, names had been scratched from the roster. Ed Webb had gone into a telephone pole after his jeep was clipped by a train. Tommy Stultz went in with a bomber at March Field in California. Singing Mike Ward got his on a home-ward-bound flight from Korea. Others had faded from the list. He couldn't place the point in his career where they had met or separated in the never ending shuffle of assignments. Now they were just names and hazily re-membered faces, but out of it one thing emerged.

Life was short; death could be sudden, and it was im-portant that while a man was alive, he should take definite stands. This included religion.

If this realization had not been borne in on him by the crash of the B-36, it would have been by something else, since he was a man of acute personal awareness, but if he could properly point a finger at any one thing which had sent him back to study Catholicism, he thought it would have been this.

There were five small Maxwells now, and he was see-ing to it that they took their parochial school training more seriously than he had. Catholicism was a religion of absolute obedience, which, as far as Joe was concerned, was all to the good. He was trying in the meantime, to establish a similar beachhead of obedience at home.

In the process of hewing three small boys down to size (the two babies were too young yet for real discipline), he often wondered if the nuns made out any better than he did.

Each boy had been given a job. Gary, eight, and the oldest, was supposed to set the table. That was all right with Gary, but he was an individualist, and he preferred doing it his way. Stacking saucers on top of cups might be perilous, but that's the way he wanted it, and he would tolerate no interference. To Gary's credit, however, Joe had to admit that so far the breakage had been slight.

John, seven, was the yard man. He was also a dreamer. He would push the mower and then lean, and when he wasn't pushing or leaning, he was lying in a chair. He could lie in a chair for an hour, kicking the wall and thinking. John was smart, but he was lazy. Joe had to keep after him.

Tim was five—not old enough to be reliable, but too old to ignore. It was Tim's job to hang up his clothes. That seemed simple enough, but the fact of the matter was that Tim just didn't care. As a result, he spent more time in the corner getting punished than any of the other children.

But no matter how long he stood there, he came away the same; untrampled, unaffected, and with an infectious grin. Joe was trying to work Tim in on the trash baskets, but so far it was no use. Tim had no more conscience about trash than he had about clothing.

Joe, his namesake, was two now, and there was the baby girl, one. It was a big family and a big task, but Joe didn't worry about it. All the boys were ambitious, and they would make the grade. John wanted to be a pilot; Gary wanted to be an engineer. Tim was the only problem. Tim wanted to be a tramp.

Joe thought about Tim as he sat there opening his flight lunch. If anybody had the makings of a first-rate tramp, Tim Maxwell did. He took out a piece of chicken and put it to his mouth. He hadn't had time to take a bite when he heard a rumbling.

# CHAPTER VI

John Cobb had just put down his computer and picked up his pencil when he heard the rumbling. Along with the rumble, there was a lurch, and the big ship seemed to stumble. Through the drawn curtains which covered the plexiglass windows, he saw a red flash. There must have been an explosion. They were in trouble. Big trouble.

John's foot hit the mike button on the floor. "What was that?"

There was split second when nobody said anything. Then Obie's voice shouted, "Fire! We're on fire!"

Cobb was sitting in his ejection seat, half-swiveled toward Joe Maxwell. Maxwell still had the drumstick holding it to his mouth. They seemed to gaze at each other for a long time, and then Jim Graves voice came through their headphones. "Bail out! Bail out! Bail out!"

The bail-out order, the most critical on the list, was one Cobb had never heard before and had hoped he never would, but here it was in his headphone and no time to think about it.

He saw Joe reach for the parachute he kept by his foot, and then John swiveled his seat into ejection position, facing dead ahead toward the nose. Quickly, he reached for the little green ball that controlled his emergency oxygen. Once he ejected, his regular oxygen supply would be cut off when the long snout-like hose which was fastened to the oxygen mask strapped across his face, pulled free from the supply within the ship itself.

The emergency oxygen is contained in a small cylindrical container, and, when the green ball is pulled, the supply inside the container is released. At the height at which they were flying—34,000 feet—oxygen is essential to survival. Without it, a man dies in about five minutes, and, because going down a 'chute takes ten or fifteen minutes, a man doesn't reach atmosphere of sufficient oxygen content to support life until it's too late.

Following the bail-out order there was a slight explosion somewhere in the pilot's position, and John knew it must be the small hatch on the side of the aircraft which allows the aircraft to depressurize. Then another explosion, this one heavier. It would be the plexiglass canopy over Obie's and Grave's heads. With the second explosion, the aircraft suddenly filled with fog and debris. Papers swirled up from his table, dust, pencils, everything, and he couldn't see.

In the normal ejection sequence, once the canopy has blown, the pilot and co-pilot eject immediately after in an almost simultaneous explosion. "They're gone!" he thought, "I'm going!"

It was important not only that he get out immediately for his own sake but because Joe Maxwell would have to come out the opening his ejection seat would make when he pulled the trigger and exploded down and out of the ship.

He kicked frantically for the pair of stirrups cocked slightly up behind either foot, which are part of the seat. They are for the purpose of holding a man in position when ejection takes place. He got his foot in the right one but couldn't find the left. He would have to let it go. He bent slightly forward and reached for the D-ring between his legs and pulled the way he'd been told to. The hatch under his seat exploded. He felt a sudden blast of cold air and could see clouds whipping by below. He was supposed to have ejected downward when the hatch blew but for some reason he hadn't. He pulled the ring harder and suddenly he went. His feet flipped from beneath him as he blasted down.

There was a moment after leaving the ship when he felt as if he were strangling. Then he knew that the reason he couldn't breathe was because the slip stream, the backward sweep of air created by the enormous speed of the plane, had caught his oxygen mask and pulled it away from his face. Swiftly he reached up and put it back in place and immediately he could breathe.

No sooner had he done this, than he began to tumble. Over and over and over he went, head down, up, down. It had all happened so fast he didn't know why, and then he realized he was still sitting in his seat. It was supposed to have fallen away from him as soon as he left the plane, but it hadn't. The shape of the thing was causing him to tumble, rather than fall straight the way he was supposed to.

As he flipped into another tumble, he knew he had to get loose. If he kept going over and over, he was going to red out. Already his eyes felt as if they were bursting from the strain, and he could see red flashes with every revolution.

A red-out produces the same result as a blackout—that is, unconsciousness. The difference is that unconsciousness in a blackout is produced by the drag of positive G forces, which drain the blood from the head, and a red-out is caused from the drag of too many negative G's, which forces blood to the head. This causes the small blood vessels and capillaries in the eyeball to hemorrhage. In both cases a man finally passes out, but instead of seeing black as he goes, he sees red, and the red is his own blood.

Cobb reached down at the seat belt, which still held him in place and jerked, and immediately he fell away from the seat. The trajectory of the seat was out from him arcing over and down, so that as he fell straight down, he was able to look up and see it for a brief and unforgettable moment, stamped on the face of the moon.

It was a quiet moment when he seemed to simply hang there in the sky, and then his body made a violent twisting motion, and he began to whip. 'Round and 'round and 'round he whipped like a ball on the end of a string. It was as if some giant had a yo-yo and was gyrating it in a series of dizzying whirls. He was sick very quickly and felt as if he would vomit. Why he was whipping he didn't know, only that he had to stop it. He put his arms out and started swimming. He had read it somewhere, and the words came back to him now almost as clearly as if he were reading them:

"To stop a heavy rotation in the air make swimming motions," it said.

Immediately after he started swimming, the rotating stopped. But he had no sooner stopped whirling than something hit him in the back. It was hard and felt like metal. It hit him again and again. Like a giant metal fist, it was beating him to death. He had to stop it somehow so he quit swimming. When he did, the beating stopped but immediately he started rotating again.

Again he started swimming, and again the something hit. In an agonizing sequence, he swam, he spun, he swam. Finally it seemed to him it would be easier to just give up. Nothing he was doing helped any. Not for any length of time.

Sick from the rotating, in brutal pain from the beating, he let himself fall. And then John Cobb saw the baby. He was standing there looking up at John the way he always did. He had on a white suit and new shoes, and his eyes were big and blue. Just as clearly he saw Cherie and even the big German shepherd, Katrina, and Tuscarora, the cat: the whole family looking up at him. He had to make one more try.

He reached down with one hand, kept swimming with

the other, found the right buckle somehow and pulled the buckle hard. Immediately, whatever it was left him falling straight away. For the first time he realized it had been his survival kit. It must have been hanging by one strap, the other strap having come loose, so that the difference in mass between the survival kit and his body imparted a revolving motion. When he swam, it fell down on top of him, and the wind currents kept flipping it against him over and over again. However it had happened, now it was over, and there was a sense of blessed relief. Then he fell through some clouds.

"Chute! Pull the chute!" he told himself. "I must be getting low!" Clouds are the first sign of the earth's denser atmosphere, and when you hit them, you know the earth isn't far below.

Just as he started to pull the ring of the chute, he saw a ground light. It was red and coming up at him very fast. Then suddenly it began moving away from him skidding out across country. When a ground light does that, it is usually too late. It means that the height which you had in order to observe it as a pinpoint directly below, has been used up so that real distance takes effect. The faster and farther it moves away, the closer you are to the ground. Was he too close now for the chute to open in time to save him?

Jerking hard at the ring of the chute, there was a moment when he stopped breathing. "Open! Open! Open!" And suddenly it did.

Or at least he supposed it had. Something had certainly happened. He had the craziest feeling that he was going back up. It was as if someone had reversed the film in a movie and put the diver back up on the board. Then he knew he wasn't going up. He was falling down. Down, down, down he fell with the first real sensation of falling since he'd bailed out of the plane.

Still there was no time to be afraid. The ground was there, and John Cobb hit it hard.

# CHAPTER VII

About the time John Cobb hit the ground, Jim Graves was halfway down. He was hanging there in the sky by means of his parachute and wondering dazedly if it had all happened the way he thought it had.

He had had his eye on the number three engine oil pressure gauge at the moment of the explosion. It was still holding, but only barely, and he had made up his mind to cut it, but as he was in the very act of reaching for the engine throttle control switch, he heard a rumble, the ship lurched slightly, and he knew that what he feared must have happened.

He heard Obie yell "Fire!" and looked immediately to his left, since that is the position of the number three engine, which he had been watching all along. From his position he could not see the side of the ship; all he could see was the backward stretch of the wing. What he saw when he looked was a heavy orange glow coming up from the root of the wing, where it attaches to the fusilage. The glow was everywhere, reflected off the high altitude mists and the bright metal of the plane. It was impossible to tell just where the fire was, but he felt it was bound to be in the fusilage.

"Bail out!" he said, "Bail out!"

Immediately following his order, he heard an explosion down in the nose. This must have been Cobb ejecting. If he had ejected, Maxwell should have been right behind him according to the bail-out procedure. Two men, then, were gone.

Almost simultaneously with the nose explosion, he felt the canopy go. A sudden blast of cold wind hit him sweeping up through his cockpit from the suction created by the two openings in the aircraft. Since only himself or Obie could jettison the canopy, he knew it must have been Obie, in which case he must have catapulted. Canopy jettisoning and ejection come one right after the other in the normal bail-out procedure.

These were all assumptions, but they were assumptions that had to be made since he could see nothing from his position either forward or back.

He knew he had twenty seconds, twenty seconds or less. That was the estimated time it took for fuel to ignite and explode. At least half that time must have elapsed. He had to get out.

He reached down under his arm and pulled at the little green ball. He should have gotten an instantaneous blast of oxygen, but he got no reaction at all. Still, there was no time to worry about it. He could pull it again on the way down. The thing that was important at the moment was to get out of the ship. He reached to his left side quickly and began the ejection sequence.

This sequence is started by pulling up the seat ejection handles. These handles are the counterparts of regular arm rests, except that they slant downward at almost a ninety-degree angle rather than extending horizontally the way the arm on a chair does. When the left handle is pulled up through a one-hundred-and-sixty-degree angle, it sets off a combination of mechanical linkages and air-operated sequences which unlock the right arm. This linkage of the two handles is important since it prevents an unintentional catapult. A person must pull both—first one and then the other—in order to eject.

When both operate properly, a number of other automatic reactions take place. The cabin is depressurized by the blowout of a hatch in the side of the ship; the ejection seat bottoms to the floor of the aircraft. (Like a barber's chair, the seat can be raised or lowered according to a man's height.) The shoulder harness locks; the control column stows, (that is, moves forward out of the way so that a man won't hit it with his knees when he is ejected); and the canopy jettisons. The final movement a man must make in order to complete the process is to squeeze a triangular-shaped trigger which is installed just below the right-hand grip. It is this trigger which sets off the charge which in turn blasts a man and his seat up and out of the plane.

In Jim's case, when he pulled the left-hand grip it only came up part way, almost to the horizontal. Still, he thought that might be far enough to have unlocked the right-hand grip, so he reached to the right and pulled up on that one. But it only came up to the same position as the left one. He decided he might not have followed the correct sequence, so he went back through it again. Left-hand grip, right-hand grip, but still neither would move all the way round in its proper arc. There was nothing left but to force them. He pulled them both up desperately, but it was no use. They both had a spongey feeling like a stretchy rubber band and remained firmly locked. This meant he couldn't eject. He would have to go out the nose hatch, the one that Cobb had used.

He reached down and flipped his safety belt loose and started climbing out of his seat, but immediately he realized he was blocked. The autopilot was unstowed, that is, pulled out of the left-hand side of the ship, where it rests when not in use. When the autopilot is unstowed, it pulls almost directly into the side of the pilot's seat. He was also blocked by the column which had not stowed automatically the way it was supposed to, and the left arm rest, which he had got partially up. He had never before been so conscious of what a big man he was and how small the seat. He couldn't move an inch in any direction. He was trapped.

The knowledge was briefly terrifying, and then he somehow twisted his body down and jackknifed beneath the autopilot, which clears the floor by some four feet. How, he did not know, but there he was in the crawlway. He was standing beside his seat, and he thought he had it made, but he had no sooner begun to turn away from the seat to proceed down the crawlway, than immediately he was jerked back. He could move neither his body nor his head. What it was that held him he could not say, and then he remembered his survival kit. It must have caught on something and was pinning his legs against the side of the platform where his seat was mounted.

The survival kit snaps onto the parachute like a seat cushion. It must be one of the straps that had caught. He reached for the right snap, so as to release himself from the kit, but found that the snap was out of reach. He could see it, but he could not touch it.

For the first time, blind panic hit him. The plane was bound to explode any second. He reached over farther, farther, stretching until his fingers almost touched the snap. But no, it was useless. It remained tantalizingly out of reach.

Suddenly, he knew he was tired. More tired than he'd ever been in his life. Something was sapping the energy out of him like draining it out of a tube. Everything was too difficult; it was simpler just to give up.

He leaned against the autopilot dumb and exhausted. How long he didn't know; perhaps a matter of seconds. Then he thought of Enel and the baby, and it was too much to give up without making a final fight. He made one final reach, and his fingers closed over the snap. Click! and he was free!

He turned swiftly. The nose hatch was dead ahead down the crawlway. He could see the heavy red glow of the flames showing through it, but as he took a step toward it his head was snatched back sharply. Something else had caught.

During the process of trying to free himself from the survival kit, he had entangled his oxygen hose. It was contorted now and twisted around the arm of the seat. For the first time he realized that the tugging at the kit snap had pulled the mask away from his face, and, with no emergency oxygen coming in from his emergency supply, he was getting almost no oxygen at all. That was why he had begun to feel so tired. He had become hypoxic.

Hypoxia is the first stage leading to complete unconsciousness. Things become blurred and hazy, and everything turns blue.

The fear of fire now left him and was replaced by fear of suffocation. He began to fight, swinging his arms, jerking his body, clawing at anything he could reach in order to pull the oxygen hose free. He didn't care what tore or broke. He had to get out.

With a final violent jerking, the hose pulled away from the mask. Now he had no oxygen at all, and if he didn't make that hatch in a hurry, he never would.

He turned down the crawlway, and as he did he saw Obie. At least he guessed it was Obie, although he could not distinguish any features. Still, it must be since the man was lurching to the right next to the rear exit hatch, and nobody else would have been that far back in the ship. This was the first time he had had any notion that he was not alone in the plane. For some reason Obie had not catapulted, and, for a minute, blind anger hit him. Why the hell hadn't Obie got out the way he was supposed to?

Then it occurred to him that Obie must be waiting for Jim to go ahead so he could go out the nose. As it was, Jim's body was blocking the narrow crawlway, and Obie couldn't get past him.

Jim started forward and suddenly saw the legs. They were propped up over something, and they didn't seem to have any body. "My God!" It hit him ,"Something's happened to Joe." For Joe it must be, lying there in the crawlway with the top of his body covered with rubbish and debris. He stood looking down at Joe. Help him? He couldn't help him. He was dying himself. In what he knew, even in his dazed and hypoxic state, was the most difficult decision he'd ever have to make, he took one step, another, and he stepped over Joe. He made a dive for the open hatch, "Joe, I'm sorry, Joe."

Then he was through the hatch, falling head down. As he dived, he closed his eyes and pulled the rip cord on his chute. He was afraid to try a delayed automatic opening, because he was too near unconsciousness. If the automatic opening device failed to work, and he wasn't conscious to pull the emergency, he would simply fall free until he hit the ground.

As he came through the hatch, his body hit the slip stream and did a violent snap. He glanced off the fusilage and something drove into his leg. An instant later he was falling, and then he felt his chute jerk open.

He put his hands to his bail-out bottle. He had to . . . had to breathe. He pulled at the green ball with both hands, but there was no apparent relief. Still he seemed to be getting a little something, maybe enough to get him down to a lower altitude, where he could take off the mask and breathe normally.

He knew that he was drifting now, falling slowly down. His body swung in the vacuum of the cold, dead sky. Everything was fuzzy. He tried to think.

Maxwell. Poor Maxwell. He didn't have a chance.

Obie? He didn't worry about Obie. Obie had been conscious and was capable of taking care of himself.

Had he done the right thing? Yes, he was sure that he had.

What the hell was he doing up here anyway? He had forty-five hundred hours flying time, and nothing had ever happened like this before.

Enel. Enel would be worried. Who would they send to tell her?

The ship must have exploded. He wondered if he could see it. Groggily he tried to look up, but the oxygen hose connected to his parachute restricted his head movement.

He looked about him and realized it was very peaceful up there. The sky was like a big black bowl lined with velvet, and it was so quiet that the quietness seemed almost alive. He would have liked to linger in that vacuum thinking nothing at all, but to think nothing was dangerous. He must get hold of himself. He would rehearse his landing procedure, all the things they'd taught him.

About then the parachute started cutting, where the straps came up between his legs. He moved back and forth a little trying to shift his weight. Then he heard a twanging, a clear singing sound like a broken violin string, and panic shot all through him. "My God! If it's one of my risers, I'll really go down." He tried to look up to check and see if all the panels of the chute were intact, but again the oxygen hose prevented it. He tried to judge then to see whether or not he was falling any faster. If he were, he couldn't tell it.

He was in some clouds now. This meant he was getting low. For the first time since he began his descent he was conscious of the cold. His hands and feet were tingling. He put his hands up under his arm pits and wiggled his legs back and forth.

Now he was through the cloud bank. He knew that meant he was low enough to have an adequate supply of oxygen. He reached up and unhooked the oxygen mask and quickly looked above him. Thank God! All the canopies were intact. Whatever it was that had broken up there hadn't been too important.

He looked down then for the first time, and he could see the ground. There was his shadow on it, and it was sweeping along like a big black bird. Backward! He was going backward! That was a dangerous way to land, but it was too late to change. He relaxed as much as he could the way he'd been told to, letting his legs hang limp, and the next thing he knew the ground had hit him hard.

# CHAPTER VIII

While Jim Graves and John Cobb were falling, two men were still in the plane. One of them didn't know it and wouldn't for some time.

Joe Maxwell had known almost nothing from the time of the bail-out order. He had felt the ship shudder, heard Cobb's "What's that?" After that Obenauf yelling, "Fire! We're on fire!" and then Graves, "Bail out! Bail out! Bail out!"

After that a nightmare filled with a rush of fear. For fifteen years he'd been flying, and he had had some close ones—the time they burst a fuel line on the take-off, and gas had sprayed all over the inside of the bomb bay; the time he and John Ballard came in on fumes over Iwakuni, Japan, and almost landed in the drink—close but never like this and in the pit of his stomach there was a cold puddle of dread.

Moving automatically, he threw the chicken down. He grabbed for his oxygen mask, which he had unsnapped in order to eat, and slapped the mask over his face. He started to pull the little green ball, but the ship was still pressurized. As yet, he didn't need any oxygen. He'd better use whatever precious time he had to get his chute on. He reached for it where it lay beside his right foot. He got it and pressed it onto his chest. It was bulky and clumsy, and he had trouble setting it in the rings. He thought he had it seated, and then he reached for the little green ball. But before he had time to pull it, there was a concussion.

He was hurtled backward, or was it forward? He was so dazed he didn't know. He only knew that he was scrambling somewhere in the crawlway, and then he passed out.

# CHAPTER IX

One man in the plane remained conscious, Lt. James Obenauf.

Just before the explosion, he had looked at his watch. There were three of them hanging on his instrument panel—two set at regular time, so that one could provide a check on the other, and one set at Zulu, Zulu being Greenwich. By the hands of his regular watches, it was 10:55. They had been out two hours and fifty minutes and were headed for Denver. He was about to put in his call to the Amarillo bomb plot to inform them that Binbrook one-six had left the bomb plot control zone after the bomb run on Dalhart, when there was a hoarse rumble. He saw a red flash over the right wing, and sparks flew in a million directions. He cocked his head back and saw flames. The right wing seemed to be covered. "Fire!" he yelled, "We're on fire!"

It seemed as if he'd no sooner said it than Jim Graves gave the order to bail out. Still there was time enough for him to be conscious of the explosion in the nose. Cobb was losing no time about getting out of there, and neither was Obie.

As soon as he heard the nose hatch blow, he began his ejection sequence. He pulled up the left arm of his seat and then the right arm, and immediately things began happening. His seat bottomed, the column stowed, and the canopy jettisoned. As it went, a blast of wind hit him, suction swift and hard. Grit and dust and debris sucked up from the nose, and something big flew past him. He guessed it was the sextant, but he didn't stop to be amazed that an object weighing ten pounds had blown past like a match stick. What was more, he had grit and sand and dust in his eyes, and the wind was tearing his head off. They were holding an air speed of about five hundred miles an hour.

He was about to squeeze the trigger in order to catapult, when he saw something below him in the crawlway.

He looked down, and it was Joe Maxwell sitting there on his hands and knees. He was shaking his head in a funny way as if he'd been hit with something. Then he turned around and started scrambling back up toward the nose.

Briefly, Obie wondered what had happened to put Maxwell back there, but whatever it was wasn't important, since Max was conscious and obviously headed up front to make his bail out. As for Graves, as far as Obie knew, Graves was already gone. In all the heavy wind and blackness, he wasn't able to see, but Jim should have gone immediately after the canopy, in which case there was nobody left but himself.

He reached for the trigger beneath the right arm and pulled it up. Braced instinctively for the blast he expected, he sat hard in his seat. But a second passed and another, and still nothing happened.

Everything was ready. Why didn't he go?

Thoughts tore through his head like hornets. He must have loused up the sequence. He went back through it deliberately; left arm, right arm, trigger. "Blow, man, blow!" But she wasn't blowing. Something had gone wrong. Desperately, he pulled the trigger, this time until it bent, but still he didn't go. There was a moment of anguish which quickly turned to fear. Die! He was going to die there. Right there in that seat.

He sat there with his hands in his lap; seconds, minutes, a liftetime. "Die! You know you're going to! Go ahead and die!" Then with a sudden abruptness he began to move. What was he doing just sitting there? Holy Cow, get out!

He reached down with quick hands and unlocked his safety belt. He slid out of his seat and caught his survival kit on something. Swiftly he snatched at it, and whatever it was let go. He stepped down from his seat, turned in the crawlway, and faced the pressure door. It was the door they used to board the plane, but he would use it to get out. He yanked hard at the lever which lets the door down and the door began to fall. It fell a little, and then it stopped. Something, he didn't know what, had jammed it. He would have to go out the nose.

The noise in the plane was like thunder, and the wind cut into him like an ice-edged saw. It was thirty-two degrees below zero. The red lights which normally light the gauges and dials were a misty glow in the heavy moisture of the atmosphere, and another red light, burning at the foot level in the crawlway, seemed to light the way to hell.

As he put his foot down and started forward, his eyes fell on something. It was lying in the crawlway directly in front of him and blocking his path. The something had long legs. It was Joe Maxwell!

For a moment Obie just stood there. What was Joe doing lying there in the crawlway all sprawled out? The last time he'd seen him he'd been headed for the nose. He looked more closely. Beside Joe lay his helmet, rocking solemn and empty like a big white skull. It must have been blasted off Joe's head by one of the explosions, or torn off in some impact. But whatever had done it wasn't important. What was important was that when it came off, it took the oxygen mask with it. At that altitude, without oxygen a man had about sixty seconds of consciousness and five minutes of life. Even now as Obie looked down at him, Joe was already dying.

His thoughts fell on one another in a tangled mess. He thought of bailing him out, but then he saw the rings. Two dull metal circles on Joe's chest stared up at him like a pair of sightless eyes. Joe hadn't gotten to put his chute on, and there was no telling where it was. It might take minutes to find it. He might not find it at all. And even if he did, he couldn't bail him out. Joe would have to be conscious in order to pull the D-ring.

He batted that one around until he came up with something else. So he'd drag Joe to the opening, pull the ring for him, and let him go!

Even as he thought it, he knew it wouldn't do. The fact was that even if he could get him down through the hatch and pull the ring for him, Joe still would have no oxygen. He'd be dead before he ever got down.

It all added up to one thing. Joe would have to die.

Having searched every possibility, Obie started to move,

but as if his foot was stuck in concrete, it refused to budge. He stood there looking down at Joe, and everything in him wanted to go. Three feet beyond where Joe lay, the hatch was open and waiting. Obie could see the dull red glow of the fire coming up through it. All he had to do was step over, and he'd be on his way down. And still he just stood there looking at Joe, and he was sick to his toes.

He'd never hated anybody. He knew that now. He'd never felt like this before in his life. Joe was between him and living, and it wasn't easy to take. He had the impulse to jerk Joe to his feet and shake him. "Wake up! Wake up! Wake up!" But shaking him wouldn't change things. The only thing to do was go. Then he thought of the kids. Five. Joe had five kids and another one on the way. As if a big spike had been driven down through him, the kids were holding him now.

He began split-second arguments derived to take care of them all: Joe's wife, the four boys and the baby girl; get them all out of the way. He didn't even know them. He didn't even know Joe. Joe was just a guy. Sometimes he saw him in his yard down the street, but he'd never even spoken except times when they flew together.

He knew that he was pleading, trying to make it right. He knew the seconds were ticking away and wondered dimly why the plane hadn't already exploded. In the final struggle, the last arguments were stronger.

He had his own battle to fight. He had a wife and a baby and another one coming. A man had to look out for himself before he looked out for anybody else.

But did he? Did he? If he did, why didn't he go?

Because he couldn't, that's why. Because he just couldn't. He could not leave a man to die when there was any chance of saving him. And in that final minute he knew that he gave up. All the arguments, all the indecisions, all the trying to make it right. There was nothing else for it. He would have to stay.

All this, from the moment when he first saw Joe until he made his decision, took maybe ten seconds. Everything came so thick and fast that it seemed to come at once, and yet each thought was a separate sliver sticking like glass in his brain.

He turned, and as he did so, there was a moment of final bargaining. If he looked out and saw things were really bad, he'd go ahead and go. He took a few steps back down the crawlway and put his hand on the arm of his seat.

Now that he had put it through the ejection sequence, the seat could still go off. The slightest jar might activate the charge and blow him to kingdom come. If, when he crawled up in it, it let go, it could cut him in two. He touched it gently, eased up onto his knees and looked back down the wing. The fire was still there blazing away sweeping in toward the fusilage. Still, for the present, the heaviest flame was limited to the outermost tip of the wing. If he could get the ship down to ten thousand feet before it came in any closer, he might get Joe to come around, and they could both bail out.

That is what he would do. He would dive her down from thirty-four thousand feet as quickly as he could. Dive her, that was, if he were able. After you went through the ejection sequence, you weren't supposed to be able to fly the controls. Part of the sequence demanded that the controls be automatically disconnected. Whether his had or not, he didn't know. Since his sequence had not been complete, there was just a chance that they had not.

He slipped around in his seat and reached out for the column. It was standing crooked, and he wrestled it back straight. Then he began to pull it toward him. The column presents a resistant force of sixty pounds. In order to pull it straight back, a man must pull hard, even under normal circumstances. Now with the wind blasting at him it was doubly difficult. What was more, he had absolutely no protection from the wind except for the small piece of metal, jutting up between his position and the pilot's, that slim twelve-by four-inch piece that was the headrest for

Jim Graves' helmet. Finally, it was cold, so cold that without his oxygen mask his face would have frozen. As it was, one hand numbed up on him as he fought the column back, and he realized for the first time that he didn't have on one of his gloves. He put his hand down in his zippered leg pocket and got out the one for his right hand. With it on, he began to pull again and, by brute force, gradually dragged the column back.

Once he had it forward, he mechanically re-engaged the controls. He unlatched the latch that stows the control column forward and held a button depressed on a handle on the right side of the seat. Still he wouldn't know whether or not it was working until he kicked the plane off autopilot. The autopilot had been set at a horizontal of thirty-four thousand feet. For now she had control of the ship; not the column. If he kicked the autopilot off and found that the controls were shot, then he had really had it. She would go into an uncontrolled dive from which it was entirely possible neither he nor Joe would get out.

It was a moment of grim decision, but he had lost all the time he could. Quickly he reached for the disconnect switch and depressed it. He eased forward on the column, and the nose dipped slightly. Working! It was working! Pushing the column forward, he began his descent.

He'd never made a dive like that one. He blistered down

from thirty-four thousand like the devil was on his tail. The altimeter dropped like a thermometer on a back porch in January. Thirty-two, thirty, twenty-eight. As it dropped, he began making his call.

"May Day! May Day! May Day! Binbrook one-six. Binbrook one-six. I've got an emergency condition."

He took his finger off the mike button and waited. Why didn't somebody answer?

"May Day! May Day! May Day!" Frantically, he called again, and then he realized he wasn't getting a background tone—that dull hum which indicates the system is connected and working. He panicked for a minute thinking the radio was out, and then he looked down and saw that his mike cord, which had come disconnected when he got out of his seat, was dangling free. When he got back in his seat, he had forgotten to plug it in. With a quick motion, he shoved it back in its socket.

Boy, he must be pretty woozy to forget a thing like that. He switched his oxygen supply up to Emergency. As if somebody had administered powerful nose drops, his head immediately cleared. Now, he had to think.

First he must cut the fuel to the number six engine. If the fire hadn't caught the wing yet, maybe he stood a chance of putting it out. He pulled number six throttle up to stop-cock and shot a quick look back down the wing.

Long licking squirts of flame projected both backward and forward and spilled on down toward the fusilage. It would be a minute before he knew whether or not cutting the fuel had cured things. Meantime, the altimeter was still falling. Twenty-six thousand, twenty-four, twenty-two, and the plane was plummeting like a hawk with a bead on a chicken.

"May Day! May Day! May Day!" This time his voice didn't bounce back at him, and he knew he was transmitting. "Binbrook one-six. Two men bailed out sixty north of Amarillo. (Already he was beginning to worry about them. Were they hurt? Were they all right? Where were they?) Two men still aboard, co-pilot and instructor-navigator. Instructor-navigator unconscious." He released the mike button and almost immediately got an answer.

"Binbrook one-six, this is Altus Tower. Understand your May Day."

He broke out in a sweat. Thank God! At last. The hard gravelly sound of the voice was like music. He repeated the message.

"Two men bailed out sixty north of Amarillo. Two still aboard, one unconscious. Going to try and bring him around at ten thousand, and both bail out somewhere close to your field."

"Roger, one-six. Understand. Transmit for ten seconds for positive position."

He pushed his mike button, and the transmitting noise came back at him with its steady hum. Altus would pick it up on their radio beam and give him a fix.

"Binbrook one-six, Altus Tower. We have you ninety west. When you reach your altitude take up a heading of zero eight five."

He looked at his altimeter. At that moment, the needle hit fifteen thousand. Another minute now and he would be at ten. He shot another look back down the wing. The bursting flame had numbed to a dull red glow. It had been an engine fire then, instead of a wing fire. With any luck at all, it would go out completely.

He looked down at Maxwell. He lay there so still. Had he already died? Had the few minutes it had taken to get him down been the ones that killed him?

Altimeter eleven thousand. Suddenly his emergency oxygen went out. There was a moment of automatic panic, and then he knew it didn't matter. At ten thousand, there was enough oxygen in the air to breath without any emergency supply.

Ten thousand. He eased back on the column, smoothly leveled off. In spite of all her vicissitudes the plane was responding nicely.

Cutting another desperate look at Maxwell, he was all but pleading. "Joe, get up. Get up!" But Joe just lay there peacefully, as if he were sleeping.

Obie took up the prescribed heading of zero eight five. Now he was barreling straight for Altus Air Force Base, just over the Texas line in Oklahoma. The wind was tearing his head off, his eyes were still full of grit. He couldn't put down his visor in order to protect them from further damage by the wind blast because that much plastic between him and the instrument panel cut his failing vision down too much. Already things were beginning to blur a little, and the figures on the board were hard to make out.

He looked again at Maxwell. "Joe! You've got to get up!" If Joe didn't come around in the next few minutes, he would have to consider making a crash landing. This would not be good. He didn't know the field at Altus. He could ram a dozen planes. Rocketing along on his belly with his wheels up, there was a good chance he'd explode.

There was one other alternative. He could leave Joe and bail out. But would he if the time came? He hadn't been able to before. Just as he began the long, hard grapple with his conscience, the lights of Altus appeared, and as if it were some kind of signal, Joe's left leg moved.

# CHAPTER X

Joe Maxwell would never remember the exact moment when he knew he was alive. He knew and yet he didn't know. Mostly he knew he was cold. A cold wind blew over him, and he felt frozen and numb. Somewhere there was a lot of roaring, and he could see a form sitting in the co-pilot's seat. It must be Obenauf. He lay there in the crawlway looking up at Obie. Something had happened but what?

He lay there for a while trying to figure it out, and then, not really knowing why he did it, he eased himself to his feet. He stumbled to the emergency exit door and saw that it had slipped down by a foot. Dimly he told himself that's why he was cold. He reached out and got hold of the lever and pulled the door back in place. Then he lay back down in the crawlway waiting to get warm.

He opened his eyes in a minute. He wasn't any warmer. He looked up at Obie and saw him moving his head. Obie was trying to tell him something, but there was an awful roaring, and if he wanted to make out what Obie was saying, he would have to put on his helmet and catch it through the earphones.

He found the helmet lying beside him and put it on his head. Still he couldn't hear Obie. There was something wrong. Carefully he took off the helmet and began to try and fix it. He fumbled with the little wires, but they wouldn't go back in. He had to thread them through a small hole and neither his numbed fingers nor his blurred vision were up to it. And he was very tired.

He put the helmet back on and lay back down in the crawlway. It was better that way.

He looked back up at Obie in a little while. Obie was still yelling. He gathered his strength for a minute and crawled over to Obie's side. He would hold onto Obenauf.

Maybe that way he could hear what Obie was saying. But he had no sooner caught hold of Obie's knee than Obie pushed him away.

He sat there trying to figure. Didn't Obie like him? No, Obie was trying to tell him something. He wondered what it was. Obie was slapping himself on the chest now and bellowing, and the cords stood out in his throat. Once, Obie took his hand off the column and slapped Joc on the chest. He made a wild motion like he was—like he was what? Flying, dancing, floating?

Joe was trying, but it didn't get through. He felt like somebody had held him up by his heels and dropped him on his head. Dazed and dumb and stupid. That's the way he felt.

And to Obie, looking down at him, that's the way he looked. Joe's eyes were big and bald and staring, as if he didn't have a brain in his head. He looked so dumb that Obie could have hit him, even though he knew it was the lack of oxygen that had done it.

"Joe! Put on your parachute!" He motioned again with his hand, but Joe just sat there staring. Boy, he could have killed him. Before that, Joe had sat there fumbling with that darn helmet until he'd wanted to slap him, turning it over and over like he was playing with a ball. Why couldn't he see? Why couldn't he? "Joe! Your chute!

Your chute!" But Joe just sat there holding onto Obie as if he were afraid Obie might leave him. Ah, crimminy. What was the use?

"Binbrook one-six, this is Altus Tower. Are you going to try and land?"

Okay. So there it was. He had to make a decision.

"Altus Tower, Binbrook one-six. I'm coming over. If it looks good maybe I'll give it a try." He was hedging, and he knew it, but he had to give them some kind of an answer.

The lights swept by beneath him as he passed over the field. He made a wide circle and started to pass over again. Then he knew he wasn't going to land, and he knew why. It had been lying there in his subconscious all the time. True, he didn't know the field, he could smash into dozens of planes, but this was the good sound business reason. There was a better one underneath.

If he had to crash land, he wanted to be as close to Pat as possible. Getting killed was a possibility, but getting bashed up was better, and, if he had to come out of it minus an arm or leg or worse, he wanted her around.

It occurred to him that this was selfish, wanting her there immediately after whatever happened, and then he decided the heck with heroics. He wasn't any hero. He hadn't asked for this jazz. They had simply handed it to him, and so he had to do it.

"Altus tower, Binbrook one-six. I can't get the instructor-navigator to put on his parachute. I'm taking the plane home."

"Binbrook one-six, Altus tower. Advise you not to. Abilene's got weather."

"Weather or no weather, I'm taking her home."

"One-six, Altus. Roger. Understand. Goodbye and good luck."

Then, just as he cut in over the field for the last time, they made a final call. "One-six, Altus. Just got a report on your two men. Major Graves and Lt. Cobb are both safe on the ground."

Part of the tight band that had been around his chest let go. He had never, from the first, stopped thinking about them. He knew that they'd be worried about him up there, and he'd been plenty worried about them. Now he put his hand to the mike button. "Altus, one-six. Tell them I'm okay. Tell Cobb I could use a good navigator right now, even him." Then he streaked back over the field. He was headed home.

# CHAPTER XI

Cobb didn't get the message from Obie for quite some time. At the moment, he was sitting in a farm-house waiting for the sheriff to come get him and take him into Dalhart. As yet, he wasn't hurting, and was wondering why. The beating he had taken on the way down, plus a very rough landing, should have done something. Maybe he was still numb.

After he hit the ground, he must have passed out. Not long; just for a minute. When he came to, he was lying there face down. The ground was rough beneath his face, and he had part of it in his mouth. Inquisitively, he put his tongue out to see if he had lost any teeth.

The teeth all seemed to be there, and slowly he raised his head. As he did so, he had the feeling that he had come home. There was something about the place that was familiar; something about the smell. Then he knew what it was. It was the smell of manure, faintly acrid and sour, and very, very close. So close, as a matter of fact, that his shoulder was in it. He had, as luck would have it, landed in a pasture, and with his unerring instinct for the ridiculous, he had landed in a cow pile.

He got up and brushed himself off, wondering how he'd been able to hit that particular spot with such accuracy, and then he looked up and saw the red light, the one he'd seen on the way down. It was practically there beside him on top of a silo. Since silos were never far from farmhouses, there must be one nearby. In a minute he would start walking until he found it.

He reached up to take off his helmet and found that he had no hands. Well, yes he had hands, but they weren't working right. They were like two pieces of wood strapped to the ends of his arms. It must have been the cold that had deadened them.

He moved his feet in his flight boots. Yes, he did have feet. He took a step or two backward. He was being pulled by his chute. It blossomed out behind him like a big orange and white flower. He turned around and faced it and began rolling it up. While he was rolling it, he thought about Joe.

Joe would never make it. He was sure of that. He'd been off oxygen sitting there eating his flight lunch, and he didn't have on his chute. Even if Joe had managed to put it on, he would have died coming down. It took ten or fifteen minutes to come down from that altitude, unless you did it the way he had, come down like a bat out of hell. He must have fallen free for thirty-two thousand feet before his chute opened. They had been at thirty-four when he bailed out, and he couldn't have had more than three or four hundred feet between him and the ground when his chute opened.

No, Joe would never make it. He was sure that Joe had died. He stopped rolling the chute a minute and said a short prayer. Then he finished rolling his chute up and put it around his neck.

He looked around him and saw a light, one he hadn't noticed before. It seemed very close to him, maybe six hundred yards, but he couldn't be certain because ground lights are deceptive at night, and actual straight-line distance was probably better than a mile. He started toward it and bumbled into a fence.

He stood there looking at the fence and knew he shouldn't cross it. Climbing over fences busted them down. He was from ranching country, and busted fences were important. They let things in that shouldn't get in, and they let the wrong things out. No, he wouldn't climb it. He would walk by the side of it until it turned, and when it did, he would turn with it.

He walked for what seemed like a mile, perhaps two miles (they told him later three), stumbling along and not thinking, just walking by the fence. The light didn't get any nearer, but it got no farther away. He guessed that he was circling, but even if he were, it shouldn't be much longer now.

Not conscious of time or anything really, he kept his eyes fastened on the light, and suddenly it was there. He had come up to a gate in the fence, which opened into a yard. As he put his hand to the gate, some dogs inside the yard started barking.

He opened the gate and went in toward the house, and the dogs came charging at him. A moment of blind anger came over him, and he wished that he could kill them. The dogs were in his way, and suddenly it was very important to tell somebody what had happened. He fought the dogs back, wishing he had a gun. He was astonished to realize that he really would have killed them if he had had one.

Then he looked up and saw a woman's face through the window of the back door. She was peering out at him, and when she saw him, her face turned frightened and scared. She must have said something, because a man's face appeared behind her. The man opened the door and looked out. "Lord, boy, what happened?"

John stood there looking at him and knew how it was going to sound. "I bailed out of an airplane." Was there another way to say it?

"You bailed out of an airplane? He bailed out of an airplane!" The man made the astonished announcement to a group gathered behind him. "Well, come in. Come in. You've got blood on your face."

Cobb walked up the back steps and stepped inside the room. There was another man and a woman and two little girls. The girls were looking at him as if he had fallen off Mars.

"Can I use your telephone? I've got to make a call."

"Sure you can use the telephone. And you can use a drink. Mother, get this boy a shot of whiskey. He looks like he can use it."

The woman disappeared in the kitchen. The man led him to the phone. "Now you sit right down here. I'll help you make your call."

John sat down and realized there was something wrong with his back. He looked up in a mirror and saw there was something wrong with his face. The flesh under his eyes was purple, and his eyeballs were all bloody. No wonder he'd scared the woman and the little girls. He was really something.

Instinctively he reached for his pipe. The pipe would really taste good. As he did so, he realized for the first time that the pipe wasn't there. The familiar hard nob of it was missing, and the pocket disturbingly empty. He sat there holding on to his pocket, and then he got hold of himself. The important thing was to get word to the field that the plane had exploded. He reached for the phone.

"Operator, I want to place a call to Colonel Perna at Dyess Air Force Base in Abilene, Texas. This is an emergency."

~~~~~~~~~~~~~~~~~~~~~~~~~~~~~~~~~~~~~~~~~~~~~~~~~~~~~~~~~~~~~~~~~~~

# CHAPTER XII

~~~~~~~~~~~~~~~~~~~~~~~~~~~~~~~~~~~~~~~~~~~~~~~~~~~~~~~~~~~~~~~~~~~

Colonel Perna was at his quarters on the base, and he was asleep. This was about the only time he was still. He had a reputation on the field; he was known as "jet." He matched the planes he commanded right down to power. It was up to him to keep his men on their toes, and by God he did. This might not win him any popularity contests, but he wasn't looking for votes.

~~~~~~~~~~~~~~~~~~~~~~~~~~~~~~~~~~~~~~~~~~~~~~~~~~~~~~~~~~~~~~~~~~~

He was famous for his temper. There had never been any hiding the rage, even when he was a kid. His mother had never held with temper being solidly Scotch-Irish, but his father was full-blooded Italian, and it was from him that the colonel had got it. It was liable to break out any time, any place and could happen to anything, even an orange.

"Who the hell can peel an orange while flying a B-47?" He had shouted that one over the phone to the man in charge of packing the flight lunches. The colonel had gotten an orange in his lunch and came near to having to eat the peeling and all. After that, there were no more oranges in the colonel's flight lunch!

"All right, Daugherty. If you don't know the color light you'll be looking for on that tanker tomorrow night, you'd damn well better stay home." Briefings were like flying into the eye of a hurricane. No matter how you had it rigged, no matter how much time you'd put on the pre-flight, he was bound to ask the one question you hadn't counted on.

"Get those Gadamn jack rabbits off the flight line! They're a menace to aviation." In the first wet season west Texas had had for seven years, the jack rabbits had flourished on the new growth of grass and danced by the dozen on the flight line at night. Morning found bodies squashed and mangled and torn from the planes which ran over them when they took off. If a rabbit had hit a propeller on one of the giant tankers, they might have deflected the blade, and even a slight deflection could very well be disastrous. Therefore, according to the colonel's orders, the men spent their time shooing away at the jack rabbits and spraying the concrete with hoses to get rid of the bloody carcasses. In the meantime, they developed a kinship with the animal world. Nothing was exempt from Perna. Even the jack rabbits caught it.

Still there was a soft spot. If you looked close, you saw it. It cropped out from behind the quick eyes, the slightly defensive chin. He worried about his wing and all the men in it. He took everything with conscience, and, the times when the planes took off en masse, he took his staff car and went out on the runway. As the giants sat in order waiting their particular turn to take off, he would circle each one like a nervous mother hen checking up on her chickens. In the heavy whine and heat blast, he drove 'round and 'round checking every rivet and seam for a possible fuel leak. If he saw anything that looked suspicious, he got out of the car and went up close, holding his hat down over his ears to keep it from being blown off by the backward blast of the engines. He had a radio in his car, from which he talked to the men in the ships. "Okay, Osman. Your tip tank is siphoning, but it should clear up after you take off."

There was more, of course, to running a wing than merely flights and flying. There were visits by inspection teams, V.I.P.'s, T.D.Y.'s, and the constant discipline of the men, for which he was a stickler. On one occasion, it was brought to his attention that some of the younger enlisted men were slipping off and going over to a neighboring town where they could get beer. Abilene is dry, so they could not get it there nor could they buy it on the base, because they were underage, so they went to the neighboring town where beer parlors didn't ask too many questions.

The colonel called them all in one afternoon; there were twenty-four of them, and they stood in a long, white-faced line knowing they were in for it. But what they didn't know and never would was that although it was Perna's job to punish them, underneath he thought they should have beer if they wanted it. A boy that was doing a man's job was entitled to a man's drink. He had spoken to his C.O. about it. "Damn it, let's do something!" But his C.O. had reminded him gently that you couldn't do much about the law, no matter what your personal opinions were. No beer for anybody until they were twenty-one. The law was definite on that.

The colonel was known not only on the base but in town as well. To the people of Abilene, he was a one-man Dyess Chamber of Commerce. He had friends among the businessmen and belonged to the country club, where he played golf on Saturdays. During tournament times, he played with the in-and out-of-towners and came in first in the open flight singles. The afternoon after the morning's triumph, with eighteen holes behind him and a silver trophy in the bag, he still couldn't keep out of it. Holding the rope to keep the crowds back, his wife watched him and mused as she had so often. "He can't help it. If he were still, I'd know he was dead."

This was the man who ran the 341st Bomb Wing and consequently the 10th Bomb Squadron, to which the men in Binbrook one-six were assigned. This was Colonel Anthony J. Perna, known almost as often by a various assortment of names: the "Blue P." because of the way he signed his name; "Anthony" or "A. J."; "The Flag," on Guam as well as at home, and during the time of a certain popular song hit, "The Purple People Eater." Nobody had more names, and nobody deserved them more. He provided the color every military outfit relishes, and which provides, as it always has, a certain esprit de corps. He was admittedly a tough man with a tough tongue and a way of getting things done. Not many would get to know him well enough to see the other side; the personal kindness, the inner conscience and concern.

When the phone rang on that April night, Perna reached for it automatically. His ears and his arms were both schooled by long practice. The "long line" was by the bedside; it was used for calls direct to his home from wing headquarters. When it rang, it was important. He said, "Colonel Perna," and instantly he was awake.

"Colonel, this is Lt. Cobb. I've just bailed out of the plane."

"Bailed out! My God, what happened?"

"One of the engines caught on fire, and I think there may have been an explosion in the fusilage. All I know is that Major Graves gave the bail-out order and I got out."

"Where are you?"

"About sixty miles from Amarillo, close to Dalhart."

"What about the others?"

"I don't know, sir. I was hoping you did."

"No, I haven't heard anything. Are you. . . ."

And then his other phone rang. It was the one used for

regular calls to town and on the field and sat beside the long line. "Hold it. I've got a call on the other phone." He said, "Colonel Perna," and a voice said, "This is Major Graves, sir. I just bailed out."

"I've got Cobb on the other line. Are you all right?"

"Yessir, I'm all right. What about the plane?"

"I don't know. I haven't heard. Where are you now?"

"I'm at a farmhouse about twenty miles from Dalhart. Anything from Joe or Obie?"

"No, until this call came in just now from Cobb, I didn't know a thing. Get the police, Jim, to come and get you and take you in to Dalhart, and we'll have somebody come up and get you later. Get in touch with Cobb. He's at. . . Hold it. Let me get the details from him."

Having gotten Cobb's number, he passed it on to Graves. "Soon as you can, get the local police out hunting for the wreck, and you'd better call the bases at Amarillo and Roswell and let them be looking too."

"Yessir, I will. Colonel, Joe Maxwell was unconscious. There was no way to get him out. He didn't have his chute on. I'm afraid he's dead."

"My God, that's terrible. Well, just hang on, Jim. We'll let you know when we hear anything."

Then the colonel hung up. In a single motion he threw

off his pajamas and began to grab for his clothes. Socks? The hell with socks. His feet squashed down in his shoes. Pants, shirt, no necktie. Someone threw him his coat. He sprinted down the hallway, out the back door. The staff car was in the driveway. He had to get down to the control room, where whatever word there was about the plane would come in first.

# CHAPTER XIII

When Jim Graves finished talking to the colonel, he put the phone back down. While he was sitting there, he had noticed there was something wrong with his left leg. There was a long torn place in his flight suit up near his thigh, and beneath the torn place there was blood stuck to his shorts and his suit. He must have rammed something in it when he bailed out—the buckle on his parachute, maybe when his body hit the fusilage. Having discovered that injury, he began to look for others. What he found was that his flight suit had been split in a number of places from the sudden blast of the wind and the opening shock of the parachute. Any pocket that had not been zippered had caught the wind and split as if it had been cut with a knife. Only the zippers remained fastened top and bottom, hanging in ragged loose-jawed lengths that held nothing together, not even themselves. All in all he looked as if somebody had thrown him in the slicing machine at the bakery and let the machine have at it.

Funny that nothing had hurt; not even the leg. After the initial glance off the fusilage, there had been no pain. Perhaps it was because he had been dazed by the landing, for in spite of the softness of the ground, he had landed pretty hard.

For a minute afterward he lay there completely flattened out. Then he began to wonder if anything was broken. He moved one arm cautiously. It seemed to be working all right, so he raised the other arm. It seemed to be working too. Left leg, right leg, everything intact. He got up and stood there, weaving around, pulled backward by the billow of his chute. Slowly he reached down and unbuckled the harness, and the chute blew away.

He looked around him then trying to get his bearings. There was a ground light in the distance, how far he couldn't say, but wherever it was, there was probably life, and that's what he was looking for. He took a step in that direction and immediately sank up to his ankles. He was standing in the middle of some kind of field, which must have been freshly plowed. Apparently there had been some recent rain, and the combination of rain and plowing had provided him with a safe landing.

As he started for the ground light, he reached up and took off his helmet. He dropped it on the ground, but he hadn't gone more than ten paces when he turned around and went back and picked it up. He might need it to identify himself as a member of the Air Force. As he walked toward the ground light, it began to come near. He hadn't been walking more than five minutes before it was directly in front of him. Now he could see quite clearly that it was a farmhouse, and there, through a window, he could see a man. He was sitting in the kitchen in his underwear, and he was reading the paper.

It seemed odd to Jim to see him sitting there reading as if everything were normal, and, for the first time since he bailed out, he felt that maybe everything was.

He stopped ten feet short of the house and hollered "Hello." There was no point in startling everybody out of their wits by walking right up on the porch. Immediately, the man put down his paper and came and opened the door. His face peered through the night at Jim, and

Jim said, "I'd like to use your phone. I've just bailed out of an airplane". He said it just like everyday, and, just like everyday, the man said, "Why sure, come in."

As Jim started to walk in the house, he looked down and saw that his boots were muddy. He hesitated, but a woman said, "That's all right. Come in."

Nobody got excited either then or later, and their complete acceptance of his presence made everything easier for him. He walked into the living room and picked up the phone. He said, "Operator, this is an emergency. I want to talk to Colonel Perna at Dyess Air Force Base in Abilene, Texas."

The operator told him that someone else had just placed a call to Dyess.

"Who was it?"

"A Lt. Cobb," she said.

"Thank God!" At least Cobb had made it. "Anybody named Obenauf?"

The operator said no.

After Perna answered, he told him the story and he then hung up. The woman had been making coffee, and now she handed him a cup. As he sat there drinking it, he again noticed his leg. While the man telephoned the sheriff, Jim examined the wound.

It was  a kind of punctured place as if somebody had

driven a nail in it and then pulled the nail to one side, but it wasn't too bad. A stitch or two should fix it up. There was more coffee while he told the man and his wife what had happened, and then the sheriff arrived. It was while they were on their way into Dalhart to meet Cobb that Jim heard the news over the sheriff's radio. "There is an unidentified planc," the announcer said, "in the air near Altus. It has an emergency condition."

A plane in the air near Altus! But that couldn't be! Anyway not his. He had had the autopilot engaged when he bailed out, and the aircraft was set on a northerly heading. Pilotless, it would have been northwest of Altus by now.

And then it hit him. The plane wasn't pilotless. Obenauf was flying her!

# CHAPTER XIV

Obenauf was flying her all right. For better or worse, boy, he was really holding her to it. He had cut his air speed to three hundred miles an hour, and that helped some. At that speed, the slip stream wasn't so bad, and by crouching as low as he could in the cockpit, he got a little protection.

In the time that had passed since he left Altus (ten minutes maybe), Maxwell wasn't much better. He had managed to plug in the cord to his earphones, so that now Obie could talk to him, even though Joe couldn't reply since his mike was out. This helped, but Max was still so groggy that most of what Obie said to him didn't seem to get through. For the most part, he just sat there beside Obie, looking up at him like a little kid. He looked so pitiful that Obie wasn't mad at him anymore. Instead of wanting to hit him, Obie felt like taking care of him. "Just sit there, old boy. Just sit there and I'll get you down."

But as anger at Maxwell had cooled, resentment towards the world had warmed. He had the feeling that everybody was against him, and "everybody" included himself. Anybody with any brains wouldn't be in this mess in the first place. He was a dope, a softey, a fathead; he was a fool and a jerk. So far he'd done only one thing he could congratulate himself on: he had gotten the fire out.

From the time he looked down the wing and saw the engine black and dead, he knew at least he wouldn't have to crash land. If everything was working the way it should —brakes, flaps, and that stuff—he would bring her in for a regular landing. He couldn't be certain that everything was working, of course, until the last minute when he actually tried them, but he went on the assumption that when he did try them, they would respond the way they should. There was no point, just now, in borrowing trouble, although there was no doubt in his mind that if he tried, they would lend it.

The thing to do now was to go over every step of the landing in the half hour he had left. He must know as he had never known, *exactly* what he was going to do when he got there. Nobody had ever flown or landed a B-47 from the co-pilot's position, with both the pilot and canopy gone. It was supposed to be impossible. And certainly no one but an idiot would try to land one in the shape both he and the plane were in. No canopy, no forward vision, failing eyesight, a dead engine, a goofy navigator-instructor, the works. Well, he was just the guy for the job. The Air Force had found their man.

Okay. Enough of the smart stuff. He had to get down to business. On the down wind leg he'd drop the gear. As soon as the plane was stabilized and had quit wobbling, he'd drop his flaps. Gear and flaps down would decrease his speed. Then, depending on wind conditions and fuel load, he'd decide about the chutes.

There are two parachutes in the tail of the B-47; one is the approach chute, a small one that is used when making a difficult approach to the field. The other is the brake chute, much larger, used any time a pilot feels he's going to need more than the regular foot pedal brakes to stop him. Right now Obie figured he'd let the approach chute alone. He didn't know about the condition of the back end of the ship. If the emergency had done anything he didn't know about, it might foul the chute, since it had to be popped in the air. If it fouled, he'd be worse off than he would be without it. The brake chute, however, he would probably use, since he would still have a good deal of fuel on board by the time he got there, and a ship full of fuel was a lot harder to land than one that was several thousand pounds lighter.

After he'd touched ground, he'd deploy the brake chute, and then he'd cut his power. One, two, and five engines until he hit sixty knots, and then he'd cut three and four. If he had to, he'd let her roll right off the runway. Beyond the runway, there was nothing but prairie. He could coast for miles.

He had the whole thing stamped on the back of his mind, when he got his first call from Fat Chance. Fat Chance is the G.C.I. station near Dyess. G.C.I. is radar and can pick up a plane and give exact position. Radio can pick up a plane and can also give position, but only by means of complicated vectoring and plotting. Radar, being quicker, more accurate, and calling for less work from the pilot, it was Fat Chance rather than Dyess that contacted him.

"Binbrook one-six, this is Fat Chance. We've got you one hundred north of Dyess on a course of one seven zero."

"Fat Chance this is one-six. Roger."

"Take up a heading of one nine zero and proceed on course."

It was good knowing that there were a couple of guys sitting down there at Fat Chance keeping him on the beam. He had a friend in the air too, although so far he'd been almost too busy to think about him. He had identified himself as Eyelash two-three and had come in on Obie's radio shortly after he left Altus. There wasn't a thing Eyelash could do to help him get down, not even guide him in. Two planes can collide in mid-air and make it look easy, but when they're looking for one another with no given rendezvous point, it's like looking for a rowboat in the middle of the ocean. No, Eyelash couldn't help him, but it helped to know that he was up there, and that someone knew what he was fighting.

Both Fat Chance and Eyelash continued to talk to him, Fat Chance giving him new headings to which, by now, he was having difficulty setting the plane. His eyes were getting steadily worse, and he could no longer make out the numbers. He merely guessed the approximate position the compass needle should take, put her on it, and hoped he was right.

There were also calls from Fort Worth and Roswell and other places which he didn't try and identify. Right now he was listening for one thing outside of Fat Chance —a call direct from Dyess. When it came, he'd know he was almost home.

It was lonely going that final twenty minutes, but for the first time since the thing happened, he had time to think about things other than Maxwell and the plane. Mainly he thought about two things: Pat and what might happen to him.

There was no discounting the seriousness of his situation. He could cover the whole thing with dry remarks to himself, but things were pretty bad. He considered the possibility of blindness and knew the possibilities were good. He was no doctor, but he knew the human eyeball was a delicate organism and could take just so much. Right now, his own felt as if the outer surface had been completely scraped away, and he would not have been surprised to put his hands up and find that they were bleeding.

Beyond the eyes, of course, there was the possibility of being maimed. If he lost an arm or a leg, they would put him on a pension, but he couldn't take much comfort in that. He would almost as soon be dead as a cripple.

As far as dying went, he didn't really believe it would happen, but there was no doubt that it could.

What would Pat do if he did die? There was the insurance, of course, but with David and the new baby coming, it wouldn't be easy.

These and other thoughts came at him cold and hard and numbing like the black bitter weather around him that had half frozen his body. His arms and neck were stiff now with tension and cold, and at times he felt almost sleepy. On the other side of the tension, there was a vast region which sought relief in unconsciousness. It would be good to sleep; just to give up. But the extra wiring they had put in seemed to be standing him in good stead. Even with the kilowatts ticking away, he should have enough reserve strength to get them back and down.

Twenty miles out from Dyess, he got his first radio call from the tower.

"Binbrook one-six, if you read Dyess Tower, come up guard channel."

"Dyess Tower, one-six. I read you."

"One-six, Dyess. Let us know what you need."

"I'm going to need plenty. I'm going to try and land, but my eyes are giving me trouble."

"Roger, understand. Right now surface winds stand at zero two zero, slightly variable ten knots."

"Roger, understand."

As close as he was now, he must soon begin his descent from the fifty-five hundred feet he had maintained ever since he left Altus. When he did, he knew he was going to run into some weather, but that couldn't be helped.

"Obenauf, this is Perna." (The colonel must have taken over in the tower.) "Are you on top of the clouds?"

"Roger, on top of the clouds, sir."

"Okay. We've got good conditions here on the field. Do you know your fuel condition?"

"The best I can see, sir, she stands at thirty-five thousand pounds."

"Okay, fine. We've got a good breeze out of the north, and you have lots of runway. Do you have your position now?"

"Roger. I have my position. Have you talked to Graves and Cobb?"

"Roger. They're both all right, and I'm counting on you to put that bird down. Just take your time if you've got the fuel. Is Maxwell able to get in the front seat to help you if you need him?"

"Sir, there is no front seat." (At this point, Obie was still working on the assumption that Graves had catapulted, in which case the seat would have gone out with him. He had not seen Graves in the crawlway as Graves had seen him.) "Besides, I'd rather Max stayed where he is in the aisle. He's still pretty groggy, and it will be a whole lot safer."

"Okay. Can you talk to him on the interphone?"

"I can talk to him, but he can't talk to me. There's something wrong with his mike."

"Roger. Just take it easy."

He was coming down now, and the weather was bad: heavy mist almost like rain and a lot of wind. "I'm in some darn bad turbulence." From the minute he hit it, things went from bad to worse. There were times when the ship took a forty to fifty degree angle, and he almost lost control.

"Roger, but we've got to get you down." The voice that spoke now from the tower was a new one. "Colonel Perna has left the tower to get a gooney bird up in the air to try and guide you in if you need him."

"Okay. Understand."

With the plane bucking and the wings wobbling, Obie brought her down to three thousand, and the new wind currents shifted new objects up from the nose. Little pieces of paper rose and crossed in front of him and clung fluttering to the instrument panel. Something caught his eye in the crawlway, and he looked down to see a clip board rise up from somewhere and come to hang beside him spinning slowly around. All he needed now was a clip board smacking him in the head! He reached out for it, but it suddenly gathered speed and headed straight for him. Blindly he ducked and heard it swish past him out into the night.

"Dyess, Binbrook one-six. I need somebody to work out my best flare."

The "best flare" is the best landing speed for a plane. A man computes a best flare by checking an aerospeed versus a weight chart, since a successful landing depends on how heavy the aircraft is, which in turn depends on the amount of fuel left in it. Ordinarily, the pilot works this out for himself, but Obie had his hands too full for that.

"Roger. We'll work it out for you. Do you know if all the fuel is out of your tip tanks?"

"Roger. All auxiliary tanks empty."

"We'll have your best flare in a minute."

By this time, things were really rocky, and he began to get very tired. It seemed as if he'd been fighting a long time. Could it really have been only forty minutes?

"Your best flare will be one-forty-three. One-four-three for landing on the figures you gave us, and you will land to the north."

"Roger, understand will land to the north at one-forty-three." He took a quick look at his fuel gauges, trying to make them out. Then he shot a glance to the right-hand side, knowing he was getting down through the weather to a point where he should be low enough to see a light.

"I believe I see a beacon!" It was dull, just a glimmer, but boy, he was glad it was there. He'd been afraid the fog would get worse, and that with almost no ceiling, he'd be on the ground before he could see it. "G.C.A., I'm crossing right over the south end of the runway. If it looks good I'm going to try and land her." But he knew that no matter how it looked, he would have to do it. His eyes would never hold out another time around.

He looked down at Maxwell. Maxwell hadn't moved for a long time. Now he was going to ask him to do something that might make the difference between a good landing and a crack-up. "Maxwell," he shouted, "get up and turn on the landing lights."

There is no landing-light switch in the co-pilot's position. They have to be turned on from the pilot's seat. Without lights, a plane can be landed, but it is tricky business. A pilot needs the steady beam of his own, the way a car needs headlights to make certain of highway bearings.

Maxwell looked at Obie blankly.

"Damn it, Max," he shouted, "get up and go turn on those lights." He knew that, although Joe was much better, he was still pretty groggy, and he had to talk rough in order to get through to him. He pointed a demanding finger in the direction of the pilot's seat, and the combination worked

Slowly, Joe got up, took a little light that plugged into the side of the ship and wove his way to the pilot's position. The light was on a long cord like the ones a mechanic uses in a garage. He was still weak, but in the last few minutes, things had begun to come clearer. He knew where they were and why they were there and that Obie had fought a long, hard fight to bring them back this far. He wanted to do what he could to help, and he could only hope that he was strong enough. Even the slightest movement seemed to take all the strength he had.

He got up to the pilot's seat and leaned over and looked inside. He didn't know a landing-light-switch from a hole in the ground. He would have to read all the labels along the right-hand side of the pilot's seat until he found the right one. He shone the little beam of the light up and down, but it was too feeble to do any good. He needed a light with a stronger beam, or he'd never find the right one.

He backed out of the seat and went back to Obie. He had to tell Obie that what he needed was a regular flashlight, but he couldn't make Obie hear him by shouting. On the off chance that Obie would understand what he meant, he took the little light and shone it in Obie's face. Obie swung his hand and knocked the light away. "Cut it out, Max!"

Maxwell stood there helpless. What was he to do? Nothing else for it. He swung the light again. This time Obie was furious. With an angry motion, he reached down in his leg pocket and handed Max a flashlight. "Here," he said, "go play with this!"

Maxwell smiled and lurched back to the pilot's seat. He knew Obie still had no idea why he had swung the light in his face, but anyway it had worked.

He leaned into the pilot's seat again and swung the strong beam on the floor of the right-hand side. There were dozens of different switches, and he had to flip the right one. He swung the light slowly, and then suddenly he saw the words, "Landing Lights," beneath two little flip switches. He reached out and touched them, and there was a responding flash. It lit up the mist outside, and he felt pretty good. He went back and stood beside Obie and gave Obie the high sign.

Obie was proud of him, but congratulations would have to wait.

"Dyess tower to Binbrook one-six. This will be the dogleg to your final approach."

This was it. He was coming in. Another sixty seconds and he would be on the ground. And then for the first time since he decided to stay with the ship, there was a terrible moment of doubt. Now that the time had come, he wasn't sure he could do it. His eyes were cut and his hands were numb, and he'd never felt so alone in his life.

It was a time for praying if there ever was one, but the fact was he didn't even think about it. There was too much of everything—too much wind, too much weather, too much fighting to keep the plane under control—to find time for prayer.

But if there wasn't time for prayer for Obie, there was time for it on the ground. There was the whole base below him—men in the tower, the hangers, the fire trucks—quiet and tense and waiting, and there were women in their homes on the base who knew that Obie was up there trying to bring a crippled plane down. One who knew both Pat and Obie went outside in the yard and climbed up on a picnic table. In her way she was getting as close to something as it was possible to get. "God," she prayed, "get him down."

Like the time he had spent looking down at Maxwell trying to make up his mind to leave him, time passed in terms of seconds rather than minutes for Obie. All he knew was that it was hard and cold and lonely and he wished it wasn't so. It was the depth of depression, desperation, a time lost, lost. And then with a suddenness he could never have anticipated, certainly never explained, something busted loose. With a sudden upsurge of confidence in which it seemed there was nothing he could not do, he caught hold of the column, eased it back, and reached for the main gear switch.

"One-six, you're one mile out."

No time now to answer. Only time to fly it.

"One-six, you're approximately fifty feet high, approaching end of runway."

Fifty feet. He took a deep breath, waiting for the touch down. All the time he was cocking his head to one side and then the other, wishing desperately that he could see ahead. With no forward vision it was like driving a car down a highway at seventy-five miles an hour with no windshield.

"Okay. Now Obie, start flying her easy." Major Reynolds was talking to him over the radio, his voice far off like an echo. "Real easy, Obie. Start easing off your power. As soon as you touch down, ease that brake chute out. Put on your brakes, Obie. Real easy now. You've got plenty of room. Get her lined up down the center line. You're looking good, buddy."

It was a tense and terrible moment. And then he had brought her down so smoothly he wasn't even sure he had touched. One minute he was up in the air, and the next, the thin long line of runway lights were spinning by on either side of him. Like a long neon line unfolding, the blue line swept past, and he held hard to the inside as he let his brake chute out. He felt the heavy tug of it and began to slow down.

The long blue line broke up into separate lights. He eased on his foot brakes, and the little lights stopped running. An instant later, Binbrook one-six stopped rolling, and he was getting out.

# CHAPTER XV

Getting? He'd never moved so fast in his life. He threw off his helmet, unbuckled his parachute, and hurtled out of his seat. He slammed into Maxwell, who was standing at the pressure door trying to let it down.

"Maxwell, hurry. Hurry. This thing may explode!" Where the idea came from he didn't know, but anyway it was sure there.

"I can't move fast. I'm too weak."

"Well, buddy, I can." Obie yanked hold of the lever, and the door fell down.

Outside, the firemen were letting down the ladder which the men used to climb up into and down out of the ship. Without the ladder, it was a good four feet to the ground, but Obie wasn't waiting. He jumped for the concrete and hit the runway running. He was headed for a ditch over to one side to protect himself from the explosion.

"Hey there, boy, watch it!" Someone caught his arm.

"Let me go!" He yanked free. "That brute might explode."

Hundreds of red and white lights were all around, surrounding him and the plane. There didn't seem to be a single space between them where he could dive through. "You can stay if you want to, but I'm heading out."

He pulled away from the fireman, and suddenly he went blind. It was just as if somebody had flipped a switch, and there he was in the dark. "Blind!" he said, "I'm blind!" He stumbled and someone caught him.

"Slow down, boy. Slow down. She's not going to explode."

"I'm blind," he repeated.

"Come over here." Someone led him off, and he could

hear them talking. "He says he's blind. He says he can't see."

"Open your eyes. Open!" They put in something cold. Whatever it was it felt good, and now he could see a little out of one eye, but the other was completely gone. They began to lead him toward a big car. It was an ambulance.

"Hey, darn it, no ambulance. I'm not going to the hospital!"

"Come on to the ambulance."

"No, darn it, I'm not going. I'm not all smashed up."

"Come on to the ambulance." The hand and voice were firm.

They led him to the ambulance, and he got inside. So far he wasn't shaking, but he knew if he went into shock he would. The thing to do to avoid shock was to put your mind on something. The book said "anything," and so he began talking very fast about whatever came to his mind.

"Hey, Max, we're in the ambulance. It's got a big red light. Have you got it going around?" He hit the driver on the back. "Hey, Max, we're in the ambulance. Can you hear the siren?"

Talking, talking, talking, he could hear himself.

"Flashlight. Where's my flashlight?" He began slapping his pockets. Right knee, left knee. No flashlight. "Oh, that's right. I gave it to Max." Checking his upper pockets.

"Hey, where's my change?" He had seventy-five cents when they took off. "Somebody got my change!" He slapped a side pocket. "Darn. I lost my stop watch. What happened to my gloves?"

"You've got them on."

"Oh, yeah," he said, "that's right." He looked out of the window of the ambulance and saw the hospital looming up. "I don't see why I have to go the hospital. I'm not all smashed up."

The ambulance made the turn into the driveway and pulled up to the rear entrance. They took him to emergency, and Obie asked for a cigarette. As a matter of fact, he'd been asking for one ever since they landed. "Hey, got a cigarette? Got a cigarette?" Seventeen thousand people and not a single smoke in the crowd. Now he asked again. "Got a cigarette?" and finally somebody found one.

All he needed now was a big slug of whiskey. He didn't like whiskey much, being a beer man himself, but he knew that the whiskey would help. He caught hold of the doctor's arm. "How about a shot?"

The doctor looked at him. "You're about to get one."

They took him upstairs and put him in bed. Dimly, he saw the nurse. She had a needle in her hand lying on a piece of cotton, and the needle was aimed at him. He flung his arm up. Not *that* kind of shot!

"Hold still!"

"No!"

"He won't let me give it to him." The nurse was talking to the doctor.

"Well, go get him a pill."

The pill came. He took it.

"Hey, Doc, are they bad?" They were looking at his eyes.

"Not bad. Not too bad. You've got a bunch of blood clots."

"Blood clots?"

"Don't worry. They'll clear up in a couple of days."

The medicine in them felt good. He was quieting down.

"Pat?" He could see her dimly as she came in the room.

"He'd better rest," the doctor said. "Here. Sit down beside him."

They put a bandage over his bad eye, and he held out his hand. Pat reached over and took it. It felt pretty good.

Twenty-four hours later, he woke up. It seemed as if he'd been sleeping for days. "Pat?" For a minute he couldn't think where he was. Then everything came back. "Pat, did I really do it?"

"Well, it says here you did." She handed him a paper. "Here. See for yourself."

He squinted up his good eye and managed to make out the headline. "CO-PILOT BRINGS IN CRIPPLED B-47," and after that, the write-up.

He put down the paper. Holy cow! He had! He looked sidewise at Pat from around the bandage. "Pat, have you seen Perna?"

"Yes, he came last night."

"Did he say anything about it?"

"He said you made a good landing."

He was thoughtful a moment. "Pat, did Perna laugh?"

"Laugh?"

"Yeah, you know."

"Come to think of it, he did. He laughed and called you a dumb punk kid."

So he hadn't been dreaming. He had heard the Blue P. laugh, which was something. As a matter of fact, the first time.

A little later they brought in Maxwell and put him in the other bed. He looked at Maxwell's hands bundled up in a hot pad lying on his chest.

"Hey, Max, how goes it?"

"Fine. It goes just fine."

"Hands hurt?"

"No, not much. They were just frostbitten. Not frozen."

"How about your head?"

"My head's all right."

"Feel tired?"

"No, not much."

"Well, buddy, I do."

There was a temporary silence.

"You know," Maxwell said, finally, "if it hadn't been for you, I'd be dead."

"Boy, I *mean* you'd be dead. You were very unconscious."

Max lay there holding to the hot pad. Finally he said, "Thanks."

Obie rolled over. "Ah, nuts. Forget it. I'd have done it for anybody."

There was another silence. Then Obie turned back to Max. "Max," he said gently, "I'm glad it turned out the way it did but—" He paused as if he were balancing an egg over concrete, "Why didn't you put on your chute so we could bail out?"

"My chute?" Max said blankly. "Why I would have. All you had to do was tell me."

Obie groaned and lay back on his pillow. He had a headache.

# EPILOGUE

The night Obie brought in the plane, two men were on the telephone, one in Nebraska and one in California. From the time headquarters at Omaha and Riverside were informed of the May Day condition of Binbrook one-six, General Thomas S. Power, Commanding General of the Strategic Air Command at Offutt Air Force Base in Nebraska, and General Archie J. Old, Commanding General of the Fifteenth Air Force at March Air Force Base in California, were hooked up on a line which tied into the tower at Dyess. For a half hour both men listened to the static calls and replies from the tower to Obenauf and from Obenauf to the tower. They were as much a part of the scene as if they'd been waiting on the flight line.

"How's his fuel load?" General Power asked of Dyess.

"He says it's okay, sir."

"Does he have his flaps down?"

"No, sir. He says he's waiting for that."

"How long has he been flying?"

"Colonel Perna says a couple of years."

"Well, all I've got to say is he must be a damn fine lad."

Thirty minutes of waiting and then, "General, he's down!"

As the telephone wires carried the message, Obie was jumping from the plane, without the slightest idea that two generals had been listening to his every move.

The tape, as recorded in the tower that night, picks up General Power's final sentence. "Operator, get me General Le May in Washington."

This, the biggest single act of heroism of the year 1958 for SAC, caught every eye and captured every heart. General Power did not wait to recognize and reward it. Having discussed it at midnight with General Le May, he advised Dyess the following morning that he would be in Abilene in twenty-four hours to award the Distinguished

Flying Cross to Lieutenant Obenauf. He wasn't sending any sub to pin the medal on him. He wanted to put his service branch's highest peacetime award on the young man himself.

Obie, with one eye still bandaged and a pair of dark glasses to protect the other, stood on the stage in the Dyess auditorium with the crew of Binbrook one-six and the commanding officers of the 341st Bomb Wing and of Dyess itself, as the Dyess Band played the Star Spangled Banner. Seven hundred and thirty people stood with him (all the auditorium will hold), and so did Pat, who was with him on the stage.

Obie keeps the medal in a velvet-lined box. Someday he will give it to David, along with the tapes and the scrapbook that bulges with newspaper clippings from all over the world. The magazines that told the story are kept in a separate stack as are the dozens of letters that poured in.

Obie doesn't have a permanent record of the telephone call that came from England—"The London Daily Times here. We have the A.P. release on Lieutenant Obenauf. Would you be so kind as to tell us what color pajamas the lieutenant is wearing?"—but he does have the Heads Up Award, a beautiful silver model of a B-47 in flight, which was presented to him a month later by General Old in California. This award is given on occasion to that person who best demonstrates the spirit and purpose of SAC. In the spring of 1959 he also received two of the nation's top three flying awards for heroism: the Cheney Award presented by President Eisenhower, and the Aviator's Valor Award presented by American Legion Aviator's Post 743. The Air Force now has him making speeches. The recent developments in satellites and missiles have had an adverse effect on Air Force enlistments. Obie has been kept busy telling audiences that it is not true that the pilot is obsolete. He ought to know.

Obie is now in command of his own B-47. Six months after the incident, he was sent to Arkansas for upgrading from co-pilot to pilot, a position that makes him one of the four youngest aircraft commanders of jet bombers in the Strategic Air Command; this out of a total of some thirty-five hundred pilots. He and Pat and David and the baby Danny, (Pat didn't get her girl!) are still at Dyess, and people still point Obie out. He's a hero whether he likes it or not, and he's slowly getting used to the idea.

There has been another change in the former Binbrook one-six crew. In November of 1958, John Cobb got orders to report to Moore Air Force Base at Mission, Texas, for pilot training. Nothing, he says, except mountain climbing, has ever given him more pleasure or satisfaction.

There is only one mark in the loss column. It is John Cobb's pipe. Whenever the men get together and rehash the incident, Cobb still talks about it. He went back to Dalhart a few days after the accident and searched all over the farm, but in the five days that had elapsed between his landing and being released from the hospital, the farmer had plowed the field. The pipe was nowhere to be found. It lies buried somewhere with the new crop, but Cobb hasn't given up hope. It turned up once before in Nevada. Maybe it will turn up again in Texas.

Since then, Jim Graves has had plenty of time to realize that even if he had cut the number three engine it wouldn't have made any difference. It was the number six engine that exploded, why, nobody knows. A fuel line just let go, and suddenly there was flame. Since he had expected trouble from number three, it was natural that he should look in that direction when the explosion occurred. The glow from under the fusilage was so diffused it was impossible to tell where it actually came from. He only knew they were in trouble and assumed it to be the worst kind.

As for the injuries the men suffered, Obie's eyes are in perfect condition and so are Joe Maxwell's hands. Jim Graves got his leg sewed up in Dalhart, and now there's nothing to show for the thrust of the buckle except a small white scar. Only two objects are still around to stand as mute reminder of what might well have been a major Air Force disaster—Joe's helmet with a dent in it where he got knocked against the step in the crawlway, and Jim's flight suit with zippers and no pockets.

Any way you look at it, it's a pretty good record.